D1612749

"Raising a child with special needs can sometimes feel like a herculean challenge. Nicole Beurkens' Life Will Get Better *provides a revolutionary approach to help your child develop skills they will carry throughout life. This easy-to-read guide will equip you with tools ranging from nutrition to movement to problem solving skills that will improve life for you and your child right now. If you're a parent of a child with attention, anxiety, mood and behavior challenges don't miss this one!"*

JJ Virgin, nutrition expert and author
The Virgin Diet and *The Sugar Impact Diet*

"Dr. Nicole Beurkens' book is a masterpiece for any parent whose child is struggling with attention, anxiety, mood or behavior challenges. Life Will Get Better *lays out the most important aspects of how to help your child get back into balance. Her cutting edge approach is truly holistic and filled with great practical tips. The strategies in this book will help set your child up for a lifetime of emotional well-being. I wish I'd had something like this to give patients years ago! Thank you Dr. Beurkens for being a beacon of light for these children and families!"*

—Sheila Kilbane, MD
Integrative Pediatrician, Charlotte, NC

"Dr. Beurkens gets down on the floor with us and our child, breaks down complex therapeutic theory into basic building blocks and makes them seem like, well ... child's play. This book is the perfect read for the parent who doesn't want just another diagnostic label, but wants to feel empowered to DO something that will help today. Real simple, real practical and for real families. I have no doubt if you employ even a few of the parenting strategies written here, your life will get better!"
—**Mantu Joshi,** author
The Resilient Parent: Everyday Wisdom for Life with Your Exceptional Child

"Nicole Beurkens really understands how to help children and families with special needs. Her years of study, clinical and practical experience are synthesized for your benefit in Life Will Get Better. Nicole paves a much-needed path of hope for families, then gives easy-to-do and powerful strategies for improving the health and happiness of all family members. Read this book, then get started or keep progressing. You'll never look back."

—**Julie Matthews,** author
Nourishing Hope for Autism

"My son was diagnosed with special needs at the age of five, and I only wish I had this brilliant book back then. It would have saved me tens of thousands of dollars and countless hours that I spent digging and searching for the answers that Dr. Beurkens has so thoughtfully compiled into one easy to use reference. From nutrition, to sleep, to strategies both the child and the parent can use to cope with difficult and sometimes frustrating issues; I can only say thank you Dr. Beurkens for putting together this lifesaver of a book!

—Pattie Ptak, parent

LIFE
WILL
GET
BETTER

Simple Solutions for Parents of
Children with Attention, Anxiety,
Mood and Behavior Challenges

Nicole Beurkens, PhD

Life Will Get Better

Copyright © Nicole Beurkens ("NB"). All rights reserved.

No part of this document may be reproduced in any form,
including photocopying or transmission electronically to any computer,
without the prior written consent of Nicole Beurkens. The information
contained in this document is proprietary to NB, and may not be used or
disclosed except as expressly authorized in writing by NB.

NB assumes no responsibility for errors or omissions that may appear in this
publication. While all attempts have been made to verify information provided in this
publication, neither the Author nor the Publisher assume any responsibility for errors,
inaccuracies or omissions. Any slights of people or organizations are unintentional.

Company names and product names mentioned in this document may
be trademarks or registered trademarks of their respective companies
and are hereby acknowledged.

NB reserves the right to change this publication at any time without notice.

This materials is provided for information only and no guarantees, promises,
representations or warranties of any kind regarding specific or general benefits, have
been or will be made by NB, its affiliates or their officers, principals, representatives,
agents or employees. NB is not responsible for, and shall have no liability for any success
or failure, acts and/or omissions, the appropriateness of the reader's decisions,
or the use of or reliance on this information.

Health/Medical Disclaimer: Information provided herein is for informational purposes only.
This information is NOT intended as a substitute for the advice provided by your physician
or other healthcare professional. Results are specific and not typical. In the event that you
use the information for your own health, you are prescribing for yourself, and for which NB
assumes no responsibility. This information is not intended to replace or be a substitute for
conventional medical care, or encourage its abandonment.

Books may be purchased in bulk by contacting the author:
Email: info@drbeurkens.com
Webpage: www.DrBeurkens.com

Cover design: Ryan M. Jones
Interior design: Rebecca Finkel, F + P Graphic Design
Editing: John Rottenberg and Judith Briles
Publisher: Sky Water Press
Creative Consultant: Judith Briles, The Book Shepherd

Library of Congress Catalog Number data on file
ebook: 978-0-9973639-0-6
paperback: 978-0-9973639-1-3

1. Special Needs   2. Learning Disorders   3. Nutrition   4. Parenting

First Edition | Printed in USA

For Bill, Caden, Jonah, Nate, and Caris

who make my life better each day

CONTENTS

part one

CHAPTER 1

LIFE *WILL* GET BETTER!

*It's never too early or too late
to implement solutions that
will move your child forward.*

Parenting under any circumstances can be a challenge. Most parents would agree that raising children can feel like the ultimate test of strength, endurance, and sanity. When a child has attention, anxiety, mood and behavior challenges, parenting can become exponentially more difficult. Many parents wonder what they have gotten themselves into!

- Is your child unpredictable and you never know what you're going to get?

- Are you dreaming of your child making it through a school week without negative phone calls or notes sent home?

- Do you feel like you are walking on eggshells around your child?

- Have you wondered if you are communicating and engaging effectively with your child?

- When you lie in bed at night do fears about your child's future keep you awake?

- Do you wonder if life will ever get better?

Since you are reading *Life Will Get Better* chances are you have one or more children struggling with challenges that prevent them from reaching their full potential. You know your child has wonderful qualities and gifts to offer the world; but on many days, the difficulties cloud the potential you know lies within.

Others may see your child only through the lens of their challenges, and sometimes even you may have a hard time remembering who your child is underneath the problems and difficulties that arise. You may spend a significant amount of time managing issues with your child's teachers and school, dealing with doctors and therapists, and just plain helping your child get through the day.

If you've been at this for awhile, you may feel frustrated and worn out from trying to give your child what he needs, but not really getting very far. You love your child more than anything, but sometimes you aren't sure how to give him his needs. It's likely you are worried not only about what is going on with your child now, but also anxious about the future and what will happen if your child's symptoms and functioning don't improve.

Parents are the most valuable resource children have, and are in the best position to implement strategies that move them forward in life.

As a clinical psychologist, nutritionist and former special education teacher, I specialize in evaluating and treating children with a wide range of developmental and mental health symptoms and diagnoses. With 20 years spent working with children and families in school, medical, and private practice settings, I understand the many dynamics involved in parenting and treating children with these challenges. My philosophy is that first and foremost these are children—they are not symptoms, problems or diagnoses.

No matter what the symptoms or issues, every child is capable of learning, growing and improving. I also know that parents are doing their best to support their children and help them improve. I see my role as helping parents better understand the underlying reasons their children are exhibiting challenging symptoms, and providing the most efficient and effective solutions to address those challenges. Parents are the most valuable resource children have, and are in the best position to implement strategies that move them forward in life. It is vital that parents be given the tools and support to impact these issues because they are the experts on their children and spend the most time with them.

I would like to answer some questions you may have before getting into the specific areas to address and solutions to implement, and lay the groundwork for what follows in the rest of this book.

Age is Unlimited

You will see that "child" is used throughout. I use this term to refer to a child of any age, from toddlers through young adults. While some of the specific solutions offered are clearly for children at the younger or older ends of that age spectrum, the majority of the content is applicable to children of all ages.

It is never too early or too late to start implementing solutions that can move your child forward!

As parents, your children will always be your children no matter their age. You have roles and responsibilities to guide them and help them achieve the most they can, even beyond the age of 18 in many cases. Whether your child is very young and just starting to exhibit difficulties, legally an adult and still living with you due to inability to move forward with independent work and living, or is somewhere in between, this book will provide you with solutions for supporting your child's development and continued growth toward improved function. Regardless of your child's age, it is never too early or too late to start implementing solutions that can move them forward!

Functioning Level

Beyond chronological age, it is important to consider the developmental level of your child. Some children may be older in years, but have impairments that cause them to *function* like a younger child. Your 10-year-old may not act like he is 10-years-old, at least not yet. It can also be the case that a child is fully capable of functioning at his age, but for various reasons may *act* like a much younger child.

Whatever the situation, it is vital that parents implement strategies that are manageable for the child's current level of functioning. You will find suggestions and examples provided throughout the book that will help you think about how to implement the solutions appropriately for your child's level of functioning.

Symptoms and Diagnoses

While some children with attention, anxiety, mood, and behavior challenges have been evaluated and received formal diagnoses, others still have not. Some parents spend a significant amount of time, energy, and money bringing their child for diagnostic evaluations only to discover that the diagnoses themselves do not provide any clear treatment path. This is common, especially in the realm of developmental and mental health disorders, and it can leave parents frustrated and lacking direction for how to actually improve their child's situation.

My experience has shown that focusing on symptoms is a more helpful way to understand a child's specific needs, as diagnoses in the realm of developmental and mental health disorders can be highly subjective. It is possible for the same child to see multiple professionals, and receive different diagnoses from each of them.

> The areas of Nutrition, Sleep, Movement, Connection and Cognition form the foundation for optimal health, development and function for your child.

Let's do a reality check: most parents are generally well aware of the symptoms their child exhibits that are causing difficulties. The aim of this book is to give parents the tools to support children with symptoms of attention, anxiety, mood and behavior challenges regardless of the specific diagnoses they may or may not have received. The best and most effective treatments are those tailored specifically to the needs of the individual child, and are not based on broad diagnoses such as autism, ADHD, or bipolar disorder. *Life Will Get Better* is for you if:

- Your child has challenges in one or more of these areas, and has received one or more clinical diagnoses.
- Your child has challenges in one or more of these areas and has been evaluated, but there was no clear outcome or diagnosis given.
- Your child has challenges in one or more of these areas, and has never been evaluated or diagnosed with any specific conditions.

The chapters to follow will provide you with clear solutions in five key areas that I have found critical for improving symptoms and functioning in children with attention, anxiety, mood and behavioral challenges. They are:

NUTRITION

SLEEP

MOVEMENT

CONNECTION

COGNITION

These areas form the foundation for optimal health, development, and function; and it is almost always the case that children with these challenges benefit from implementing solutions in all five of the areas. Rarely are the symptoms that children exhibit caused by a single factor, nor are they solved by a single intervention. These challenges are multi-faceted, generally with many different underlying factors, and require approaches in a variety of areas.

You may not have previously considered one or more of these solution areas as applicable to your child; and it is very possible that professionals have not provided you with information about one or more of them that would bring change and relief. Whether you think an area is applicable to your child or not, I encourage you to read the information provided here in order to better understand how some of these solutions may be key to improving your child's condition. You may be surprised how simple shifts in the areas of nutrition, sleep, movement, connection (relationships), and cognition (thinking skills) can make a profound difference in your child's development and function.

Life Will Get Better is designed so that you can read it from cover to cover, but feel free to read the chapters in any order you prefer; and while the solutions within each chapter can be implemented independently, you may choose to implement multiple solutions simultaneously. Please do not feel overwhelmed. Remember, you do not need to do everything all at once! Start with what seems most applicable and doable for you and your child.

Throughout *Life Will Get Better* you will read stories of various patients and families with whom I have had the privilege of working over the last 20 years. The names have been changed, but the stories are real and illustrate how the various concepts and strategies can be used in real life situations with children of various ages and functioning levels. It is my hope that their stories will not only help you see how you might implement these solutions in your own situation, but also give you hope and inspire you to what is possible for your child and family.

Before beginning your journey with me, it is important for you to understand that you are not to blame for your child's difficulties and challenges. What is essential for you to grasp, and believe, is that *you have the power to make life better for your child and your family.*

Let's get started!

part two: **nutrition**

CHAPTER 2

NUTRITION MATTERS

*There is an undeniable connection between
food, mood, and behavior.*

The saying that "you are what you eat" is absolutely true on many levels. The food you put in your body has a massive impact on how well your brain and body function. When poor quality foods are eaten, you generally do not perform as well as you do when you eat foods with better nutritional quality. Research has repeatedly demonstrated connections between the foods we eat and our moods, thoughts and behaviors.[1] This is true for both adults and children.

If your child struggles with inattention, irritability, anxiety, hyperactivity, oppositional behavior, learning disorders, aggression, or related challenges, then food and nutrition may be part of the problem—and also part of the solution. Nutrition-related issues can range from not eating enough foods with quality vitamins and minerals, to poor absorption of nutrients in foods, to the body reacting negatively to specific foods. Because food can be both the problem and the solution, knowing how to identify potential problems and implement specific solutions is key to addressing the symptoms your child experiences.

> If your child struggles with inattention, irritability, anxiety, hyperactivity, oppositional behavior, learning disorders, aggression, or related challenges, then food and nutrition may be part of the problem—and also part of the solution.

While there are sometimes clear physical indicators that a child has nutrition-related issues, such as poor physical growth or specific food allergies, many are not as easy to spot. Below are less obvious signs and symptoms that can indicate nutrition-related problems for children:

- Dark circles under eyes
- Chronically dry, flaky skin or eczema
- Red cheeks and/or ears
- Irritability
- Poor focus and attention
- Obsessive thoughts and behaviors
- Anxiety and/or panic
- Depression
- Mood swings
- Aggressive behavior
- Weight regulation problems—overweight or difficulty gaining weight
- Sleep problems
- Chronic coughing, sneezing and/or congestion

- Frequent illnesses
- Sensory processing problems such as tactile sensitivity or auditory sensitivity
- Appetite regulation problems—no appetite or constantly hungry
- Hyperactivity
- Fatigue and sluggishness
- Picky eating
- Constipation
- Day and/or night wetting (beyond the typical age of toilet training)

The types of symptoms and challenges discussed in *Life Will Get Better* are typically considered "mental health" issues by the experts. As a result, there tends to be little attention paid to the physiological aspects of these difficulties. Research has demonstrated that physical health, and specifically nutrition-related issues, can be at the root of these mental health symptoms.[2] Newer scientific research is demonstrating the significant connection between the human gut (gastrointestinal system) and brain function.[3]

> Nutrition is a foundational component in alleviating attention, anxiety, mood, and behavior challenges for the vast majority of children.

In fact, the gut is now referred to as the "second brain" because of how intricately the gut and brain communicate. The gut comprises the bulk of your immune system, and also is the location where serotonin and other important neurochemicals are produced. The microorganisms in your gut play a critical role in brain function including your mood, behavior and cognition. Your brain cannot perform as well as it should when your gut is out of balance, poorly absorbs nutrients, is over-run by harmful microorganisms, or has other problems. Your child is no different. Nutrition is a key component in addressing gut health so that the brain can function more optimally.

While traditional mental health approaches such as cognitive and behavioral strategies can be important components of treatment, little progress will be made if the underlying physical factors are not identified and addressed. Nutrition is a foundational component in alleviating attention, anxiety, mood and behavior challenges for the vast majority of children.

Some children need to improve their intake of essential nutrients across the board, while others benefit from reducing intake of artificial chemicals in their diet. Some need to correct bacterial imbalances in the gut, while others function better when identified foods are removed from their diet.

Regardless of the specific nutrition issues that may be present, supporting children to eat a diet full of as many nutrient-dense foods as possible should be the goal. This section will help you to start thinking about whether nutrition factors may be a component of your child's challenges, and will provide starting points for improving food intake for your child and family.

CHAPTER 3

SUGAR AND ARTIFICIAL SWEETENERS

*Beware of sugar-filled foods and drinks
masquerading as "healthy" options,
especially flavored milks, fruit snacks,
yogurts, and juices.*

Sugar consumption is a controversial topic for sure! There is no question that increased sugar intake makes people more prone to physical problems such as obesity, diabetes, and other inflammatory health conditions. What is less clear is the impact sugar consumption has on your mood, behavior and cognition. Research thus far has been inconclusive about the direct role of sugar consumption on ADHD, mood disorders, and learning challenges.[1] However, it's known that high sugar intake causes blood sugar levels to rise and fall throughout the day, commonly known as "sugar highs" and "sugar crashes." Rapid increases and decreases in blood sugar levels are definitely linked to instability in mood, cognition and energy levels. This is especially the case for children. [2]

Given that increased sugar intake is a clear problem for physical well-being, and potentially a problem for brain health and mental functioning; reducing the amount of sugar children consume is a logical strategy. While consuming small amounts of added sugar may be appropriate, the average intake of sugar consumed by most people on a daily basis far exceeds what is supportive of health. Limiting sugar consumption is a simple strategy parents can utilize to support appropriate weight, stabilize mood, promote attention and concentration, and improve overall physical health.

One specific sugar to watch out for is high-fructose corn syrup (HFCS). This is a highly processed corn-based sugar present in many packaged foods and beverages. If a food or drink has HFCS in it, the nutritional quality of the product is likely very low. HFCS may also be problematic beyond the sugar factor as it is made from corn, which is known to cause gastrointestinal difficulties, allergy issues and other health challenges for some children. Aiming for higher quality foods that support your child's nutrition and health status means avoiding HFCS whenever possible.

Simple shifts for reducing sugar intake include:

- Kids can't eat what isn't provided for them, so focus on making healthier choices readily available. Reduce the number of sugar-filled snack and beverage options accessible for your child, while increasing the amount of healthier options on hand.

- Beware of sugar-filled foods and drinks masquerading as "healthy" options, especially flavored milks, fruit snacks, yogurts and juices. These generally have very high amounts of sugar and are far from healthy options.

- Slowly start incorporating more fruits and vegetables into your child's snacks and meals, as this will help fill them up and provide a defense against eating more sugary options. For example, carrots or apple slices with peanut butter are a better choice than peanut butter cookies or packaged crackers with peanut butter.

- Provide water as a beverage instead of soda or juice.

- Read labels, and purchase foods that do not list some form of sugar in the first three ingredients. Avoid products with high fructose corn syrup anywhere in the ingredient list.

▶ **Key Take-Away**
Reducing sugar intake is a sensible strategy to improve your child's physical, cognitive and emotional health.

Avoid Artificial Sweeteners

Artificial sweeteners are chemicals used to sweeten foods and beverages without the calories associated with sugar. They go by a variety of names including aspartame, sucralose, acesulfame potassium, neotame, saccharin, cyclamate, and aspartame-acesulfame salt.

Most of them can be found in virtually all foods and drinks labeled with the terms "diet" or "light," as well as in many popular sports drinks, energy drinks, and juices. These chemicals initially gained popularity because people thought they would help them avoid the weight gain associated with sugar intake. However, it's now known that artificial sweeteners actually make people gain and retain weight over the long term.[3] They alter the internal mechanisms that allow people to know when they are full, and tend to make people crave sweets even more than eating regular sugar.

Sugar substitutes cause wide-ranging mental and physical problems for children and adults.

In addition to these problems, research has shown that these chemicals can cause or exacerbate a host of physical and neurological problems.[4] Many children and adults experience symptoms ranging from chronic headaches to joint pain and irritability that can be caused by intake of these chemical sweeteners. Research has demonstrated that these chemicals can be particularly problematic for people with mood disorders.[5]

Based on the mounting evidence that these sugar substitutes cause wide-ranging mental and physical problems for children and adults, I recommend that these be removed from the diet. Even if behavioral symptoms do not improve, there is no benefit to ingesting these chemicals. You and your children are better off not to consume them!

You may be wondering what kinds of sweeteners are safe to consume. In general, natural sugar is a safe option when used in moderation. Obviously, there are many problems associated with consumption of large amounts of sugar; so using sugar sparingly is key. However, if you are making the choice between splurging on the diet soda or a soda sweetened with real sugar, I would encourage choosing the real sugar sweetened option.

There are many natural no-to-low calorie sweeteners you may want to explore, including stevia, xylitol and erythritol. These can be used when cooking, and can also be found in an increasing number of packaged food items. Look for beverages sweetened with these natural ingredients instead of artificial sweeteners in order to avoid the excess calories and toxic effects.

EMMA'S STORY

Emma came to see me at age 20 when she had just finished her sophomore year of college. She had a long history of depression, anxiety, sleep problems, and chronic headaches, and had been taking multiple prescription psychiatric drugs for eight years with only minimal improvements.

> Emma wanted to do a test to see if the avoidance of artificial sweeteners was really making any difference.

She was a long-time diet soda drinker, as this was what was available growing up. While Emma was not initially interested in changing her eating habits, she was willing to stop drinking diet beverages to see if any of her symptoms would improve. After one week, Emma reported that her chronic headaches were much improved. A month later, she had increased energy, was sleeping better, and felt that her mood was lifting.

Because we were implementing other treatments at the same time, Emma wanted to do a test to see if the avoidance of artificial sweeteners was really making any difference. She went back to drinking diet drinks again for a few days to see if her symptoms would return. Within 24 hours, her headaches were worse again, and she felt more moody and irritable.

Emma was convinced that artificial sweeteners were triggering some of her symptoms, and she has since given them up for good. While other treatments were certainly important in reducing her symptoms, the removal of artificial sweeteners was key to improving her overall physical and mental health.

> ### ▶ Key Take-Away
> Artificial sweeteners have no benefit for physical or mental health, and have the potential to cause many problematic symptoms including inattention, hyperactivity, irritability, headaches, anxiety, and more. Avoid these ingredients in foods and beverages: aspartame, sucralose, acesulfame potassium, neotame, saccharin, splenda, cyclamate, and aspartame-acesulfame salt.

CHAPTER 4

CHEMICALS AND ALLERGENS

Research has shown that artificial additives in foods
are associated with significant health concerns.

When you look at the labels of most packaged food and beverage items available in the United States, you will find a long list of ingredients you struggle to pronounce and certainly would not use in your own kitchen. This is because many of the ingredients found in processed foods are artificial chemicals and dyes that are not found in real foods.

Chemical preservatives, such as sodium benzoate, are added to keep foods edible for lengthy periods of time. Colorful artificial dyes, such as Red 40 and Yellow 5, are added to increase the visual appeal of foods—particularly those marketed to children. Other chemicals, such as MSG, are added to enhance the flavor and texture of foods.

The general rule to reduce and eliminate these artificial ingredients in your family's diet is to avoid purchasing foods with ingredients you have never heard of, cannot pronounce, or wouldn't cook with in your own kitchen.

Research has shown that many of these artificial additives are associated with significant health concerns, particularly when consumed in larger doses over time.[1] Artificial food dyes have been linked to many problems including hyperactivity, inattention, eczema, asthma, and allergies.[2] Food flavor additives such as MSG have been shown to increase anxiety, hyperactivity, headaches, and physical restlessness in sensitive individuals.[3]

While consumption of artificial flavorings, preservatives and dyes is clearly not the cause of symptoms such as hyperactivity, irritability or inattention for all children, there is ample evidence that some children's symptoms are negatively impacted by consumption of these chemicals. There is mounting scientific evidence that the sheer amount of these chemicals being consumed by children today as compared to just 20 years ago has dramatically increased, and that this is cause for concern related to numerous health risks.[4] Given that these artificial ingredients provide no health benefits, and may cause health problems for the majority of people, it is a wise strategy to work toward eliminating these chemicals in children's diets.

It is interesting to note that while many other countries have banned these ingredients in foods sold in their countries, here in the US they remain approved by the FDA for consumption. The US allows companies to use many more artificial colorants in foods as compared to other countries.

Common artificial food dyes used in the US include Blue #1 and #2, Green #3, Red #3 and #40, Yellow #5 and #6, and Citrus Red #2. Companies producing packaged food products in multiple countries must adhere to the approved list of ingredients for each country. That means many of the packaged food items produced for sale in the United States contain a host of unhealthy flavor enhancers, dyes, and other ingredients that are not contained in these same foods sold in other countries.

If these companies can manufacture these food products with healthier ingredients for sale in other countries, then why not in the U.S.? It's an important question to ask yourself when shopping for processed food items at the store, and I encourage you to purchase items manufactured by companies using higher quality, healthier ingredients.

The general rule for reducing and eliminating these artificial ingredients in your family's diet is to avoid purchasing foods with ingredients you have never heard of, cannot pronounce, or wouldn't cook with in your own kitchen. These ingredients generally do not contain any nutritional benefits, and may exacerbate physical or mental health problems. The good news is that more companies are being responsive to these concerns and altering their products to contain less artificial ingredients. You won't have to make everything from scratch in your kitchen in order to feed your children foods free of artificial flavors, colors and preservatives!

Get familiar with reading labels, and choose items with real (not artificial) ingredients. Some parents worry it will be more expensive, but that does not need to be the case. It is entirely possible to feed your family on a budget with healthy foods free of artificial and potentially dangerous chemicals. While some additional time may need to go into shopping and preparing foods, the results will be worth it if your child is better able to focus, regulate behavior, sleep, and function.

DYLAN'S STORY

Dylan and his parents had been seeing me for almost a year due to ongoing concerns with emotional and behavioral regulation. He had been born very prematurely and had a host of developmental challenges since birth. Now at seven years old, he was still having significant issues with impulsivity, anxiety, irritability, and generally disruptive behavior at home and school. While he had made some progress as a result of working with his parents to implement supportive developmental and behavior strategies, Dylan still had many more difficult days than I wanted to see.

Raising the option of nutrition strategies early in our work together, his parents were not open to changing anything about their food intake at that time. They were concerned that Dylan, already a smaller child, would refuse new food options. Convinced that their busy schedules would not allow for them to focus on healthier food choices for Dylan, and that it would be too costly, they initially refused to look at changing his diet. When I again raised the idea after almost a year of using other strategies, they were ready to consider it.

They were frustrated with how challenging it was to manage him on a daily basis, and wanted to see if changes to his food intake would make any difference. We discussed potential starting points; and based on what I knew about Dylan and his history, I recommended they first try switching to foods that did not contain artificial preservatives and dyes. This was a challenge, as most of the foods they provided Dylan were processed and had a host of chemicals and dyes in them. We developed lists of items to swap, and I helped them learn to read food labels carefully. I also taught them how to shop for more whole natural foods, such as produce instead of packaged options, and provided some quick, simple recipes I thought they would enjoy.

> By the two-week mark, there was no question that Dylan was significantly improved across the board with his behavior and mood.

Dylan was initially unhappy with his new food options, as he had grown used to consuming things like fruit punch, candy, Pop-Tarts, and Trix yogurt on a regular basis. I supported his parents in implementing the connection strategies they had learned to weather the storms of Dylan's food-related refusals for the first few days. He quickly realized that he was not going to have those items anymore, and resigned himself to eating the many foods that were available.

His mother contacted me five days into their food experiment to report that Dylan already seemed more calm and obedient at home. By the two-week mark, there was no question that Dylan was significantly improved across the board with his behavior and mood. He was also sleeping through the night, which had been a challenge for years. His parents were completely convinced that removing the artificial chemicals and dyes in his foods was making a positive difference for him. They went on to implement additional nutrition strategies that continued to benefit him. The changes to his diet helped his system regulate to the point that all the other beneficial strategies they were using in terms of parenting and cognitive strategies were more consistently effective.

Through the years he has had some slip-ups with eating things containing harmful dyes and chemicals, and it is almost always quickly apparent in his behavior. After a few days of not eating the offending foods he is back to his new normal, which allows Dylan and his parents to enjoy a much happier life together.

> ▶ **Key Take-Away**
> Avoid feeding children foods and beverages with artificial dyes, preservatives and other chemicals, as they have been shown to worsen attention, mood and behavior symptoms.

Identify and Treat Food Allergies & Sensitivities

While most people are familiar with the concept of food allergies, food sensitivities or intolerances are less widely known and understood. Over the past decade an increasing number of people have developed adverse reactions to foods containing gluten and other allergens, which is heightening awareness of food-related symptoms. The reality is that while food is typically something your body tolerates well, specific foods can cause the body's immune system to react in negative ways. When this happens the person can experience a host of symptoms ranging from unpleasant to life threatening. Children with attention, anxiety, mood, and behavior symptoms may have underlying food allergies or sensitivities that are causing or perpetuating these symptoms.[5]

It is important to understand the difference between food allergies and food sensitivities, also referred to as food intolerances, as both are immune system responses to foods that show up in different ways. The term allergy is typically used when the person has an immediate immune response to food exposure, such as when a child eats peanuts and has difficulty breathing or breaks out in hives.

> The eight most common food allergens in the United States are wheat, dairy, soy, eggs, peanuts, tree nuts, fish, and shellfish.

Food allergies are typically easy to spot because there is a clear immediate reaction such as difficulty breathing, swelling of the face, hives, vomiting, or other clear immediate symptoms. Food sensitivities or intolerances, on the other hand, are delayed immune reactions to ingesting certain substances. These sensitivities can show up as eczema, irritability, headaches, mood changes, brain fog, sleep and other problems after hours, days, or weeks of ingesting the offending food. This delayed immune response makes food sensitivities more difficult to recognize, and many children have symptoms resulting from delayed immune responses to foods that go unidentified and therefore untreated.

There are two primary methods for determining the presence of food sensitivities: blood testing and an elimination diet. While blood testing can be helpful to determine specific food sensitivities, it is not definitive and can fail to uncover some problematic foods.

The gold-standard method for determining food sensitivities is to implement an elimination diet, where foods are systematically excluded to determine which items may be causing or exacerbating symptoms. This method allows children and families to specifically determine which foods need to be removed from the diet over the longer term. The eight most common food allergens in the United States are wheat, dairy, soy, eggs, peanuts, tree nuts, fish, and shellfish. While these constitute the majority of food allergies and sensitivities, other possibilities include corn, specific fruits or vegetables, chocolate, pork, and beef.

It is important to determine if a child's symptoms are connected to food allergies or sensitivities, as this is a specific issue that can be treated by simply removing offending foods. There are specific physical and emotional signs that can indicate the presence of food sensitivities, so it is helpful to work with professionals with knowledge in this area. Investigating food sensitivities is especially pertinent for children who have not made consistent progress with other treatments or whose challenges seem to be worsening over time.

PATRICK'S STORY

Patrick first came to see me at age 15 when he was discharged from inpatient psychiatric treatment for the third time in a year. He was severely depressed, highly anxious, and had been suicidal for many months. His mother reported that he had been very intelligent since he was a young child, but had always struggled to fit in, had a very low frustration tolerance, and was chronically worried about irrational things.

It was clear to me that there were numerous physiologically based issues going on.

Patrick had taken a turn for the worse over the prior year. He had developed significant depression in addition to his other symptoms. He had become unable to attend school and needed constant supervision to ensure his safety. They came to my office after seeing multiple other diagnosticians and therapists over the years. Patrick was taking five psychiatric drugs at the time, yet was still highly symptomatic. After taking a detailed history and spending time with him during our initial appointment, it was clear to me that there were numerous physiologically based issues going on. I collaborated with his primary care physician, who was willing to run blood work to look at nutrient levels and signs of immune dysfunction.

His lab results showed what I had suspected: Patrick was exhibiting a very high level of immune response and some significant nutrient deficiencies. Further lab testing revealed a number of specific food sensitivities. Patrick and his mother were so desperate to see improvements that they were willing to immediately implement all nutritional recommendations. They removed all offending foods from his diet, which included gluten, dairy, eggs and others. We also started targeted nutrient supplementation in collaboration with his primary care physician and prescribing psychiatrist. Within two weeks, Patrick reported feeling somewhat better.

Three months after removing specific foods from his diet, his symptoms were significantly improved to the point that his psychiatrist was willing to begin reducing some of his medications. After 24 months of a tailored food plan, neurofeedback, nutritional supplementation, and cognitive-behavior therapy, Patrick is functioning better than he ever has before.

He has returned to school, is getting excellent grades, spends time with his friends, and is no longer depressed, chronically anxious or suicidal. All but one of his medications has been discontinued, and that medication is being slowly weaned over time. Patrick continues to maintain a diet free of foods that exacerbate his symptoms, although he can have some offending foods periodically without major problems.

Specific food sensitivities were most certainly at the root of his symptoms, and removing them was key to helping Patrick feel and function better.

▶ **Key Take-Away**
Some children have specific food allergies and sensitivities that negatively impact their functioning. Identifying and removing these specific foods can lead to significant improvements in attention, anxiety, mood, and behavior.

CHAPTER 5

BACK TO BASICS

Protein, fruits and vegetables, and water are critical to support brain alertness and steady energy all day long.

Breakfast has long been touted as "the most important meal of the day," yet many do not eat a breakfast that supports brain and body function. Research has shown that it's common for children to skip breakfast altogether, and those who do eat something tend to grab high carbohydrate/sugar options.[1] Protein is critical to support brain alertness and steady energy all day long, and a breakfast containing good quality protein sets children up for success throughout the day at school.

> Sugar spikes and crashes can lead to irritability, hyperactivity, brain fog, moodiness, impulsivity, poor attention, and headaches.

While it may seem easier to pour a bowl of cereal or grab a piece of white toast, these options are generally low quality carbohydrates that leave kids in a "sugar crash" mode relatively quickly.

Carbohydrate-filled breakfast foods tend of have a high glycemic load, meaning the body converts them to sugar very quickly. This sets kids up for a surge in blood sugar and insulin that then crashes quickly. These sugar spikes and crashes can lead to irritability, hyper-activity, brain fog, moodiness, impulsivity, poor attention, and headaches.

Children who eat breakfasts with lower glycemic load have more energy and better cognitive performance by the end of the morning than children eating higher glycemic load breakfasts.[2] Breakfasts containing protein, healthy fats, and whole grain carbo-hydrates have lower glycemic loads, which means they support more steady energy for physical and mental stability throughout the morning.

There are many ways to provide children with a protein-packed breakfast without taking a ton of time.

- While we tend to think of certain items as being "breakfast foods," the reality is that any food can be eaten at any time of day. Meats, fish, quinoa, cheese, nuts and seeds may not seem like traditional breakfast foods, but they are easy sources of protein to start the day. For a really quick breakfast option, simply heat and serve leftovers from dinner the night before!

- Protein shakes are a simple way to start the day off right. Use a high-quality protein powder and ingredients such as coconut milk, leafy greens, and fruits to boost nutritional value.

- Toasted whole grain bread with protein-rich toppings can be easy and delicious. Nut butter is an easy choice, and there are many delicious and nutritious options beyond peanut butter, including almond butter, cashew butter, and sunbutter. Add some banana slices on top for even more nutritional value. You can also try toppings such as smashed avocado, eggs, sliced cheese,or cream cheese with whole fruits or jam.

The key to a breakfast like this is to choose high-quality whole grain bread, and avoid white breads or processed breads with high sugar content and little nutritional value.

- Eggs are a protein-packed option that can be made in multiple ways: hard-boiled, scrambled, fried, or deviled. Some of these can be made the night before for a quicker morning routine. Omelets or scrambles with cheese and veggies are another great nutrient-packed option.

- Yogurt without added sugar is another high-protein option. Mix in whole fruits, nuts, and even whole grains such as oats for a quick nutritious breakfast.

DANIEL'S STORY

13-year-old Daniel had been diagnosed with ASD and ADHD since the age of four. While he was capable of being in a general education classroom at school, his constant struggles with attention and concentration left him lagging behind his peers both academically and socially. Daniel didn't like to eat much, especially in the mornings. When he did eat breakfast, it was something along the lines of a Pop-Tart or muffin washed down with juice. He had constant complaints of fatigue, despite the fact that he was sleeping sufficient hours at night.

Teachers reported that Daniel was sluggish in the classroom, especially in the mornings. He fell asleep in class sometimes, and generally was having difficulty concentrating long enough to get his work done.

Daniel knew that this was a problem, and was willing to try some diet changes to see if his performance at school could improve. He and his mother implemented the first change by improving the quality of his breakfasts. They switched from high glycemic load pastries and juices to whole grain toast, eggs, bananas and water.

Within the first week, Daniel reported that he felt more awake in the mornings at school, and wasn't falling asleep at his desk. After two weeks, his mother asked his teachers for an update, and they reported that he seemed more alert and focused, and was getting more of his morning work finished in class. The simple strategy of improving the nutritional quality of Daniel's breakfast, with a specific focus on including more protein, had a positive impact on his learning and behavior in school.

> **▶ Key Take-Away**
> Start the day with a high quality protein-packed breakfast to support attention, mood, behavior, and learning throughout the morning at home and school.

Eat More Fruits & Vegetables

Your parents used to tell you to eat your fruits and veggies, and they were right! This simple strategy involves increasing intake of these important foods in order to support health and functioning, while also providing a great alternative to some of the less healthy foods you want to reduce in your child's diet. Fruits and vegetables contain a wide variety of important vitamins, minerals and phytonutrients that support optimal health and brain function. The fiber content of fruits and vegetables helps you stay full longer so that you are less likely to eat poor quality food between meals, and helps stabilize blood sugar levels to support sustained brain function throughout the day.

Increasing fruit and vegetable consumption is an excellent way to support appropriate levels of the vitamins and minerals needed for optimal growth and development. The goal is to eat all the colors of the rainbow regularly, as a rainbow of colors in produce provides an optimal balance of beneficial nutrients. Fruits and vegetables contain important phytonutrients that help protect against disease and retain your health and function as you age. They also contain a host of important vitamins and minerals needed for countless functions throughout the body. Research has shown that children with attention, anxiety, mood, and behavior challenges are often deficient in one or more nutrients.[3] They may also need higher intakes of specific vitamins and minerals in order to support appropriate function.[4] Increasing fruit and vegetable intake is a simple way to provide these nutrients daily.

You may be feeling like it is an impossible challenge to get your child to eat his veggies and fruits! Some children do balk when offered fruits and vegetables, mainly because they are not used to eating them. It can be helpful to slowly start incorporating more produce into your child's diet. Here are some ideas to encourage your child to eat more fruits and vegetables:

- *Have various produce options* available for snacks through-out the day, including familiar and unfamiliar items.

- *Prepare fruits and vegetables in various ways* so your child can try different preparations. For example, carrots can be served raw, boiled, grilled, sliced into long strips or into coin shapes, and with a wide variety of toppings.

- *Offer them with various dips* such as almond or peanut butter, salad dressings, or hummus.

- *Cut them into fun shapes or characters.* Encourage your child to play with his food so he can explore the scents, textures and visual aesthetics of the food before eating it.

- *Model eating more fruits and vegetables yourself.* Your child is more likely to eat produce if he sees his parents and other trusted adults doing so.

- *Pair fruits and veggies with your child's preferred foods* so he can try something he isn't sure about while having the security of something on the plate he knows he enjoys

- *Keep encouraging your child to try new fruits and vegetables,* as it can take 10 or more times of trying a new food before he can truly decide if he likes it or not. Perseverance is often needed when it comes to trying new foods!

- *Make smoothies and popsicles with fruits and veggies.* Experiment with different combinations to find your child's favorites.

- *Don't force your child to try new fruits and vegetables,* but don't offer unhealthy alternatives either. If you provide produce options for a snack and your child does not eat them, simply tell your child that food will be available at the next meal.

• *An older child or young adult* often benefits from increased knowledge about the role of fruits and vegetables in supporting symptom improvement. Provide him with information about the nutrients in various types of produce, and why higher consumption of these items may help him feel and function better.

When purchasing produce, it is important to buy the highest quality items you can afford. Organic is often best simply because the plants are not sprayed with toxic pesticides and other chemicals. However, produce of any type is definitely better than none at all! If you purchase non-organic produce, it is important to wash it well to remove as much of the chemical residue as possible. The Environmental Working Group has lists online called the Dirty Dozen and Clean Fifteen that provide helpful guidance on which produce items to prioritize in terms of organic versus non-organic.

> ▶ **Key Take-Away**
> Increasing fruit and vegetable intake helps ensure beneficial levels of essential vitamins, minerals and phytonutrients, and reduces the amount of less-healthy food consumed over the course of the day.

Drink Water Throughout the Day

Drinking more water is one of the simplest strategies to improve learning, mood and behavior for children and adults! It's no secret that water is an important part of a healthy diet, but few people actually consume enough each day. Most children ingest enough water via foods and drinks that they do not have clear dehydration. However, drinking less water than recommended results in subclinical dehydration that can have negative effects on the brain and body.

Children should be encouraged to drink water as their primary beverage throughout the day. Water provides the hydration their brains and bodies need without any other ingredients that could cause problems.

Research has shown that drinking water has clear positive effects on memory and cognitive performance, as well as physical stamina and overall health.[5] It's documented that increasing water consumption has positive effects on mood and mood stability.[6] Many chronic physiological symptoms are also connected to mild to moderate dehydration, including headaches, constipation and fatigue. In addition, the more water you drink the less you drink poor-quality options such as sodas and sports drinks.

Children should be encouraged to drink water as their primary beverage throughout the day. Water provides the hydration their brains and bodies need without any other ingredients that could cause problems. At school, children should be allowed to have water bottles they can sip on throughout the day, or at a minimum, frequent water breaks to the drinking fountain should be allowed. For additional impact at school or during homework time, use a water bottle that requires your child to suck on the straw or spout to get water out. A strong sucking pattern with the mouth supports calming and mental focus. Children involved in sports or other physically demanding activities require even more water in order to avoid dehydration-related mental and physical symptoms.

Recommended daily fluid intake:[7]

    5-8 year olds – 5 glasses/1 liter

    9-12 year olds – 7 glasses/1.5 liters

    13+ years – 8-10 glasses/2 liters

Ideas to make the switch to water easier:

- Cold water is generally preferred, so keep a pitcher of water in the refrigerator at all times. Use ice in water bottles or freeze water bottles half-full overnight, and then top off with water in the morning so they stay cold longer during the school day.

- Add natural fruits to flavor water: lemons, limes and oranges are easy to squeeze in water for a burst of healthy flavor. Put some frozen berries in water, freeze fruits in ice cubes, or put fresh fruit slices in the water.

- Use fun cups, straws and water bottles to increase visual appeal.

- Remove beverages such as sugary juices, soda pops, and artificial sports drinks from the house so water is the available option.

- Gradually switch to water by diluting beverages such as juice over time. Use more water to less juice each week to help your child get used to less sweet drinks.

▶ **Key Take-Away**

Drink more water! Increasing water consumption throughout the day can have a positive impact on mood, behavior, learning, and physical health.

CHAPTER 6

SPECIFIC NUTRIENTS

*Increasing Omega-3 intake through food
and supplements is an excellent way
to improve the health of the entire family.*

One of the most researched nutritional approaches to improve attention, mood and behavior for children is adding more Omega-3 fatty acids to the diet through food and supplementation. Most studies show that children with these conditions experience symptom improvement when they receive Omega-3 supplementation.[1] Research has also demonstrated that many of these children have abnormally low levels of Omega-3s when compared to the general population, making it an appropriate target for supplementation.[2]

Omega-3 and Omega-6 are "essential fatty acids," meaning they are required for proper brain and body function. They must come from your diet because your body cannot make them in large enough amounts for optimal function. Research has shown that many people are deficient in Omega-3s in particular,[3] which is unfortunate since they are essential for brain function. In the United States, people tend to get an overabundance of Omega-6s in their diets via oils and processed foods. Having an appropriate balance of Omegas is important, as too much Omega-6 can lead to suboptimal health. The standard American diet has very little Omega-3, so making sure you have adequate levels of this nutrient is important.

Consuming high quality fish and seafood products on a regular basis is the best way to improve Omega-3 levels through the diet.

Omega-3s are an important component of cell membranes (the barrier of the cell) and stimulate anti-inflammatory effects in the body. They surround the cells of the brain and nervous system, providing important protection and function for these cells. Omega-3s are found in the following types of foods: fish, seafood, grass-fed animals, eggs from chickens eating natural diets, dairy products from grass-fed cows, flaxseed, chia seed, walnuts and some other nuts, and avocados.

The long-chain Omega-3 fatty acids are most important and are known as EPA and DHA. These long-chain fatty acids are obtained through food or supplements and are found only in marine sources such as fish, shellfish, algae, and seaweed. Consuming high quality fish and seafood products on a regular basis is the best way to improve Omega-3 levels through the diet.

While high quality seafood is the best way to increase Omega-3 intake via diet, a simpler way for many is to increase Omega-3 levels through taking supplements. These supplements have been shown in research studies to be very safe with no significant risks. When using Omega-3 supplements, sometimes referred to as fish oil supplements, it is essential to use high quality products. The fish oil needs to be from a reputable company that conducts rigorous quality and safety testing to ensure there are not contaminants such as mercury or other dangerous substances in the fish oil.

These supplements come in various forms including liquid, capsules or gummies. Note that the capsule or liquid forms are most cost-effective, as the gummies or other chewable products require taking many more at once to reach the needed dose. It is also generally the case that gummy products contain a high amount of sugar and other ingredients you should avoid. Keeping capsules or liquid in the refrigerator helps reduce any bad taste that can occur with fish oil, and they are also available with various added flavorings. It is not wise to mix fish oil supplements with water or milk, as the oil does not combine well with these liquids! However, the oil can be mixed into smoothies or other foods to assist with taste and texture tolerance as needed.

When selecting a fish oil supplement, it is important to look for a combination of DHA and EPA as both have been shown to be necessary for symptom improvement. Dosing varies depending on the age and size of the individual, so work with a knowledgeable healthcare provider familiar with Omega-3 supplementation to determine the best dosage for your child. The general concern is that the dose may be too low to have an impact, so high dosages may be necessary for a particular individual.

The recommended intake of Omega-3s for healthy individuals ranges from 200mg daily for infants up to 500mg for adolescents and adults. Studies of children with behavior, attention, mood, and developmental symptoms have used dosing up to many thousands of milligrams of Omega-3s daily.[4] At very high doses, some people can have mild digestive side effects including "fishy burps" (after-taste), loose stools, or stomach upset. These symptoms are rare and generally mild. If they occur at all, it is advisable to try a different brand/type of fish oil, take the supplement with food, or change the time of day the supplement is taken. If your child is on any prescription medication, especially blood thinners, check with his/her physician before using Omega-3 supplements.

It generally takes months of increased Omega-3 intake for the full benefits to be achieved. Many notice improvements more quickly than that—some within a few weeks. When using this strategy, it is important to stick with it even if symptom improvements are not immediately recognized. It is worth noting that there are numerous benefits for physical health as well. Omega-3s are vital for supporting heart health, reducing inflammation throughout the body, and supporting blood pressure regulation to name just a few. Increasing Omega-3 intake through food and supplements is an excellent way to improve the health of the entire family.

BRADLEY'S STORY

Bradley was five years old when his parents first brought him to see me for symptoms including inattention and hyperactivity. They were concerned that he may have ADHD, as this had been suggested by his kindergarten teacher given his behavioral struggles in school. His parents were very hesitant to put him on medication, as they were concerned about the side effects in the short and long term.

One of the potential treatments they had read about was Omega-3 fatty acids, and they were interested in trying this approach. With their physician's blessing, Bradley started taking 1,200mg of high quality fish oil daily. They also started slowly shifting from a diet high in processed foods to better quality whole foods. His parents began reporting some subtle improvements in Bradley's functioning at home during the first month of taking the fish oil. He was slower to get upset, less hyperactive in the evening hours, and seemed to be happier.

> His parents began reporting some subtle improvements in Bradley's functioning at home during the first month of taking the fish oil.

Three months after starting the fish oil, Bradley's parents had a conference with his teacher at school. She reported that Bradley was doing better across the board, although still had some episodes of impulsivity and low frustration tolerance. He was able to sit and focus for longer periods, and was completing more of his work as a result. She also noted that he was getting into trouble less with peers, and was actually engaging in more constructive activities with friends in and out of the classroom.

We continued to implement additional nutritional, cognitive and behavioral strategies to support Bradley's functioning over time, but it was clear that increasing Omega-3 fatty acids was an important part of addressing his symptoms.

Key Take-Away

Increasing Omega-3 fatty acid intake through foods and supplements supports improvements in mood, attention, behavior, and learning.

Nutritional Supplement Support

It is not uncommon for children with attention, anxiety, mood, and behavior challenges to have various specific nutrient deficiencies. Some of these children have clear-cut abnormally low levels of specific nutrients, while others have subclinical deficiencies that still require attention. Some of the more common nutrients that research has shown are connected to these symptoms in children include iron, zinc, magnesium, Omega-3 fatty acids, calcium, and B vitamins.[5]

There are various methods for assessing nutrient deficiencies including physical examination, clinical observations, diet analysis, blood work, and taking a thorough history. It is not uncommon for children to receive a clean bill of health from a primary care physician despite having symptoms that indicate nutrient deficiencies. This typically occurs because many physicians are unaware of the importance of assessing nutrient status in regard to developmental, emotional and behavioral symptoms.

It is important to work with a professional who can investigate your child's symptoms through the lens of nutrition in order to determine if specific nutrient supplementation and other customized nutrition supports are appropriate. When considering nutritional supplements, consultation with your child's healthcare provider(s) is recommended to discuss potential risks and benefits, particularly if your child is taking prescription medications.

Below are examples of some connections between specific symptoms and nutrients that may be important to evaluate for your child:

- Low appetite – Zinc

- Hyperactivity – Magnesium, B vitamins, Calcium

- Fatigue, sluggish – Iron, B vitamins

- Poor attention and concentration – Omega-3 fatty acids, Iron

- Irritability/Moody – Omega-3 fatty acids, Magnesium, B vitamins, Vitamin D

- Tactile sensitivity – Omega-3 fatty acids

- Anxiety – Magnesium, Omega-3 fatty acids, Vitamin D

- Chewing/mouthing inedible items – Zinc

- Difficulty waking in the morning – B vitamins

There are many specific nutrients that can be connected to learning, behavior and emotional symptoms. Obtaining appropriate levels of nutrients through food should be a top priority. However, some are unable to get enough nutrient support through their food intake. It is also the case that people with symptoms often require nutrient levels significantly higher than what can be reasonably obtained via food intake. For these individuals, specific nutrient supplementation is important and necessary to support symptom improvement. Some children may benefit from specific types of multivitamins, while others may need a variety of specific nutrient formulations. There are many excellent products available that can be easily given to children who cannot yet swallow pills or who are highly suspicious of taking anything new.

Beyond specific vitamins and minerals there are other supplement supports that may be valuable additions to your child's treatment program. Many children with developmental and mental health challenges have bacterial imbalances in their gut that negatively impact their function. Probiotics, enzymes and antifungal supplements may be beneficial to improve gut health and reduce symptoms. Supplementing with specific amino acids can be very helpful for a variety of symptoms including anxiety, panic, obsessive thoughts and behaviors, mood instability, and food cravings. Identifying the connections between symptoms and nutrients should be a critical part of treatment planning for children with attention, anxiety, mood, and behavior challenges. Using the correct nutrients in the right formulas and at the proper doses can be some of the simplest solutions for these childhood challenges.

ZACH'S STORY

When I first met Zach he was six years old, but looked like he was three given his size. His parents brought him to see me because his behavior was getting more aggressive and unpredictable, and he had a very low tolerance for anything that didn't go his way. Zach also had never slept well, and had an extremely limited diet. They reported that Zach never seemed hungry, and it was a struggle to get him to eat even the few things he liked.

Parent training, neurofeedback, and movement strategies were also implemented over time as part of Zach's treatment plan.

One of the first things I discussed with Zach's parents was the need to get him eating more and sleeping better so he could physically grow and so that his brain function was better supported. Zach's non-existent appetite was an indicator of low zinc levels, and testing confirmed this. He started taking 20mg of a well-tolerated form of zinc daily, and within two weeks his appetite started to increase. The dose was altered slightly over the next few months to achieve consistently appropriate appetite and food intake. A specific form of melatonin was recommended along with other strategies and routines to support his sleep, and within a week he was falling asleep and staying asleep through the night.

Parent training, neurofeedback, and movement strategies were also implemented over time as part of Zach's treatment plan. As a result of these individually tailored approaches, Zach is now growing physically, has an appropriate quantity and quality of sleep, no longer has frequent episodes of aggressive or dysregulated behavior, and is a happier child at home and school.

> **Key Take-Away**
> Specific nutritional supplements at the proper doses can be an important component of treating attention, anxiety, mood, and behavior challenges in children and young adults.

CHAPTER 7

INVOLVE YOUR CHILDREN IN FOOD-RELATED ACTIVITIES

Involve your children in as many food-related
activities as possible to expand their palates.

B y now you are hopefully convinced that the food your child eats makes a significant difference for his or her functioning. However, you may be concerned about how to make changes to your child's current diet. The most frequent objection from parents regarding feeding their children healthier foods is the concern that the kids won't like it and therefore won't eat it. It can be frustrating for parents to change their child's eating habits when they are met with constant resistance. Know that this is a very solvable problem, as there are many effective strategies to help children eat more of the foods you want them to eat.

One of the best ways to help children expand their palates is to involve them in as many food-related activities as possible. The more they are exposed to the sights, sounds, smells, textures, and tastes of food, the more comfortable they will be with trying new things. Here are some specific suggestions for providing food-related opportunities to children on a regular basis:

- *Bring your child grocery shopping* with you so they see the many varieties of foods available. They can help you find items throughout the store, cross things off the list, put produce in bags, etc. You can even have them do a simple scavenger hunt where they find new items you want them to try.

- *Visit a local farmer's market together.* This is a great way to expose children to all the various types of fruits and vegetables that grow during various seasons. They can touch items, pick out something new that looks interesting to them, and even do some sampling.

- *Look through recipe books* and choose items that look interesting. There are many recipe books geared toward children, as well as websites with a wide variety of recipe options. This is an excellent way to expose children to the many different ways to prepare foods.

- *Prepare snacks together.* Give your child experience with basic food-related tasks such as pouring, spreading, or counting out specific numbers of items.

- *Play with food.* Encourage your child to explore new food items by stacking them, making animals or characters with them, or just moving them around on the plate or table. Physical exploration is often a first step in the process of helping children get comfortable with the idea of putting something new in their mouths.

- *Cook a dish or meal together.* Cooking provides many opportunities for your child to learn new skills, work through a step-by-step process, be in a helping role, and gain exposure to the sensory aspects of foods. Even if the food is not something your child is willing to eat, having them participate in making it forms a bridge to getting more comfortable around new and different foods. Younger and more impaired children can take a role as simple as helping to stir something, while older children can participate in more complex roles such as cutting, measuring, and putting things in the oven.

- *Serve food during meals.* While your child may not eat everything that is put on the table during a meal, serving items to others provides another opportunity to get comfortable with the smells, sights, sounds, and textures of foods. Give your child the role of scooping food onto each person's plate, including their own. They may eat it or they may not, but this is another opportunity to engage with the food in a positive way.

- *Talk about the food you are eating* to spotlight various features such as how it smells, what it feels like when you touch it, what it feels like in your mouth, the sounds it makes when you bite into it, the ways it tastes, and more. This helps your child anticipate sensations so as to reduce anxiety about it.

Using words also helps your child connect the logical brain to the emotional brain, which is very helpful for reducing anxiety and thinking through the process rationally instead of responding in an emotionally reactive manner.

- *Clean up meals together.* Every child can take a role in clearing the table, doing the dishes, putting away left over foods, etc. This provides another opportunity for being competent in a helping role, while also building comfort around food-related items and processes.

Parents need to be prepared to persevere in order to support children to become healthier eaters, and not take food refusal personally.

In general, it is best not to force your child to eat things that make them uncomfortable. While some children may eat the things being forced upon them in the moment, rarely does this strategy lead to children who truly enjoy a variety of foods. Don't be surprised when food battles continue on a regular basis. A more effective approach is to continually expose your child to the foods you want them to eat, even if they initially reject the items. The food battles will subside.

Pairing a preferred food with a non-preferred food is helpful, as it ensures there is always something comfortable on your child's plate. I generally encourage parents not to be short-order cooks, meaning they should prepare one meal for everyone instead of cooking specific things according to each child's preferences. However, you can make sure there is at least something included in the meal that your child will eat.

For snacks, I encourage parents to offer choices among the things they would like their child to eat, but allow the child to choose not to eat if they don't like the choices. The vast majority of children will not turn down food to the point where it constitutes a health problem. While there are a few children who will refuse food to the point of starving themselves, this is very uncommon. Most will eat something from the options offered.

Parents need to be prepared to persevere in order to support children to become healthier eaters, and not take food refusal personally. It is a process, and one that can develop slowly over time. Start taking small steps toward healthier eating patterns for your child by implementing one or two strategies at a time, and working from there. Any change you make toward helping your child eat food that is supportive of brain and body health is a step in the right direction!

▶ **Key Take-Away**

Moving children toward healthier eating habits is a process that happens over time. Small steps implemented consistently will help your child expand food preferences and eat more of the foods that support optimal health and function.

part three: **sleep**

CHAPTER 8

THE IMPORTANCE
OF SLEEP

Identifying and treating sleep problems is
essential to improve any problematic symptoms
your child may be experiencing.

Everyone recognizes the importance of sleep! If you have struggled to sleep for even one night you can attest to how stressful it is and the ways it negatively impacts functioning the next day! Sleep is essential for physical health and proper brain function, and this is even truer for children than it is for adults.

If a child is not getting the appropriate amount and quality of sleep each night, a number of problematic symptoms can arise including inattention, anxiety, irritability, and challenging behaviors. Research has shown that poor sleep quality and duration can negatively impact virtually all aspects of brain function including memory, problem solving, communication, mood, decision-making, stress level, emotional regulation, and the ability to learn new information.[1] Physical health is also negatively impacted by poor sleep, and research has demonstrated that chronic sleep problems can cause and exacerbate many physical conditions.[2]

Prescription and over the counter medications can seem like an easy solution, but they do not address the root of the issue and can cause additional problems.

If your child never sleeps well, chances are you are well aware it is a problem! When your child does not fall asleep or stay asleep easily, your own sleep as a parent is negatively impacted. There are some sleep problems that may not be as readily apparent but still require attention. The following are red flags for sleep problems in children:

- Struggle to fall asleep at night
- Restless sleep as evidenced by lots of movement during sleep, covers strewn around the bed/room, finding the child on the floor or in various positions in the bed upon waking
- Snoring
- Periodic gasping or choking during sleep
- Waking during the night for longer than a few minutes at a time for reasons other than to use the bathroom
- Frequent nightmares or night terrors
- Frequent sleep talking and/or sleep walking
- Bedwetting
- Hyperactive during the day

- Frequently tired during the day, even though they may have slept for an appropriate number of hours
- Irritability
- Trouble waking in the morning
- Problems with attention and concentration
- Learning problems
- Memory problems

If your child is experiencing any of these sleep-related issues, it is important to raise these concerns with your child's healthcare provider. Identifying and treating sleep problems is essential to improve any problematic symptoms your child may be experiencing, and there is a limited amount of benefit that will come from other treatment approaches if sleep problems are not properly addressed.

Beware of advice indicating that medications will solve sleep problems. There are numerous medications frequently prescribed to get children to sleep, but research shows these medications can change patterns of sleep in detrimental ways.[3] While children may fall asleep and stay asleep, these medications change the structure of their sleep cycles so they do not obtain the amount of deep restorative sleep they need. These medications also have the potential to cause a host of additional negative side effects, making them a less desirable choice for improving sleep in children (and adults for that matter).

When a child is not sleeping well, it is important to intervene to improve both quality and amount of sleep. Prescription and over-the-counter-medications can seem like an easy solution, but they do not address the root of the issue and can cause additional problems.

Strategies such as consistent routines, avoiding foods that cause sleeplessness, and utilizing specific supplements can improve sleep without the use of drugs.

If these first-line interventions don't work, there are numerous other strategies such as individualized nutrition supports, behavioral interventions, and neurofeedback that can successfully treat sleep issues. Some children may require a sleep medicine consultation to address medical reasons for sleeplessness. The good news is that there are many effective non-medication solutions to improve sleep for children, and to make the process easier for parents and families. This section will provide you with a variety of options to get you started with addressing sleep-related issues.

Quantity & Quality of Sleep Matters

Many parents are aware that sleep is important for children, but they may be confused about how much sleep their child should actually be getting each night. The optimum amount of sleep varies somewhat from one person to another, but there are some general guidelines based on age. In order to determine if your child is getting enough sleep, it is helpful to know what is typical and recommended for people at various ages. The National Sleep Foundation recommends the following: [4]

- Newborns (0-3 months): 14-17 hours

- Infants (4-11 months): 12-15 hours

- Toddlers (1-2 years): 11-14 hours

- Preschoolers (3-5): 10-13 hours

- School age children (6-13): 9-11 hours

- Teenagers (14-17): 8-10 hours

- Younger adults (18-25): 7-9 hours

- Adults (26-64): 7-9 hours

- Older adults (65+): 7-8 hours

These sleep times are recommended, but parents need to take individual child factors into account when determining what is ideal for their particular child. While each child may require somewhat more or less than the recommendations, these ranges provide parents with a good guide for determining whether their child is sleeping too little or too much. If a child's sleep duration is well outside the recommended range, it is important to talk with the child's health-care provider(s) to determine potential causes of sleep issues, as well as solutions. A child who sleeps too much or not enough is likely not functioning optimally during the day.

> Sleep should be something that occurs easily, and does not cause undue stress or effort for you or your child.

Beyond the amount of sleep a child gets each night, the quality of the sleep is also critical. A child may be sleeping for an appropriate number of hours, but the quality of sleep may be poor. The child may be awakened numerous times in the night due to physical restlessness, breathing difficulties, or environmental factors.

When this occurs, neither the child nor the parents may realize it is happening. A child with sleep apnea, for example, can stop breathing for brief periods each hour of the night. It may not seem that the child is awake, but the brain is coming out of sleep constantly in order to ensure that breathing continues. This causes much disrupted sleep that leads to fatigue the next day, even though it appears the child slept a decent number of hours the night before.

Any disruption in the amount or quality of sleep your child is getting should be addressed, as it may be causing or exacerbating symptoms. Sleep should be something that occurs easily, and does not cause undue stress or effort for you or your child. The goal is to implement strategies that allow your child to fall asleep easily, stay asleep for an appropriate number of hours, and have good quality sleep throughout the night so s/he wakes feeling refreshed and able to function throughout the day.

▶ **Key Take-Away**

The quantity and quality of your child's sleep matter. Knowing how much sleep your child should be getting allows you to determine if your child is sleeping too little or too much.

CHAPTER 9

BEFORE BEDTIME

Children whose engines are running
100 miles per hour right up until parents
try to put them to bed will likely struggle
to get to sleep.

One of the key strategies for helping children sleep better is to establish and maintain a consistent bedtime routine. Children thrive on routines, even though they sometimes seem to enjoy chaos more! When children can predict what is coming, they feel more secure and their central nervous system is better able to relax. Sleep specialists have long touted consistent bedtime routines as critical for helping children fall asleep and stay asleep at night, and research has shown how important these routines are for improving the quality and amount of sleep.[1]

Here are the steps to develop a consistent bedtime routine:

1. *Determine what tasks and activities need to be completed prior to going to sleep.* Tasks may include showering/bathing,

having a small snack, brushing teeth, reading books, laying out clothes for the next day, and saying good night to family members. Make a list of everything that you would like your child to do leading up to falling asleep.

2. *Put the tasks and activities in an order that makes the most sense.* For example, if your child is going to have a small snack before bed, then teeth brushing should occur after that. Taking a bath earlier in the evening may make sense to promote calming for some children, while older kids may benefit from taking a shower closer to bedtime.

3. *Decide what time the bedtime routine should begin.* The easiest way to do this is to determine what time you would like your child in bed, and then work your way backward through the bedtime routine tasks to find an appropriate starting point. Most families find it works best to start the bedtime routine about 45-60 minutes before bedtime. This allows enough time to complete everything without rushing, and promotes a sense of calm leading up to sleep.

4. *Once you have determined the activities for your bedtime routine and their timing, begin to consistently implement the plan each night.* There will obviously be the occasional night when the usual routine won't work, such as during special events or holidays. But in general, this routine should be implemented virtually every night without fail. The basic routine should stay the same regardless of what else is going on. There may be nights when you decide to have your child go to bed earlier or later than usual, but the routine leading up to bedtime should stay the same.

5. *Tweak the bedtime routine as needed over time.* You can alter the order of activities, timing, or the tasks you include if something is not working well. Keep working at it until you find the flow of tasks and the timing that works best for your child and family.

One additional element of consistency to consider in relation to sleep is going to bed and waking at the same time each day. It is easier for your brain to get into a healthy cycle of sleep and waking when you go to bed at the same general time each night, and wake at approximately the same time each morning. This is typically not as much an issue with young children, but teen and young adult children may try to get by with little sleep during the week and then sleep until the afternoon on weekends. A haphazard sleep schedule is not conducive to developing overall healthy sleep patterns.

Going to bed at the same time each night, and waking at the same time each morning may be necessary to support appropriate sleep for your child. This and the other elements of a consistent sleep routine can make a positive difference in regulating sleep and wake cycles for your child.

> ▶ **Key Take-Away**
> Keep the routine leading up to bedtime consistent in order to pro-
> vide the predictability and order a child's brain and body needs to
> prepare for sleep.

Calming Activities in the Evening

Within the consistent bedtime routine discussed in the previous section, it is important to help the child physically and mentally wind down from the pace of the day in order to support falling asleep.

This can be a challenge for some children, particularly those who tend to be hyperactive and struggle to calm down on their own in the evening. These children often seek out loud highly active activities even as the evening wears on. It is important for parents to help children regulate their activity levels throughout the day, but especially in the evening to assist with settling down for sleep.

Children whose engines are running 100 miles per hour right up until parents try to put them to bed will likely struggle to get to sleep. It is best to avoid physically stimulating activities such as playing chase/running games, wrestling, tickle games, etc., as these types of activities activate the child's system rather than helping them settle down. The same goes for video games, television, and other screen activities, which have been shown to stimulate rather than calm the nervous system. Save these kinds of activities earlier in the day when you are not trying to help your child sleep!

Calming your child's nervous system in the hours leading up to bedtime is important for supporting good quantity and quality of sleep. Here are some specific activity suggestions for promoting calm and relaxation as your child gets ready for bedtime:

- *A warm bath can promote calm and relaxation.* Make sure your child is not getting too active in the bath with vigorous splashing, playing with noisy toys in the tub, etc. For young children who require assistance with bathing, make sure you are using slow firm motions when washing their body. Epsom salts can be used in the bath water for added calming benefits. Start with ½ cup of Epsom salts and work up to 1-2 cups as tolerated.

- *Essential oils such as lavender, roman chamomile, ylang ylang, and vetiver are known to have calming properties* that help some people settle down for sleep. There are many commercially available essential oil blends specifically created to support calming and sleep. Rubbing these oils on your child's feet before bedtime can be a helpful part of a calming bedtime routine.

- *Deep pressure activities can help calm your child's sensory system before bed.* Make "sandwiches" by having your child lie between two pillows, and providing firm even pressure over the body. Create a "burrito" by rolling your child semi-tightly in a large blanket to provide even pressure along the entire body. Giving firm hugs and squeezes can also be calming for a child. If you are reading together, have your child sit in a beanbag chair or other item that surrounds and supports the body. Place blankets or pillows on top for added pressure.

- *Give your child a massage before bed to promote calming and relaxation.* There are many books and programs available that teach parents specific techniques on how to provide massage for children. Take your child's cues as to the level of firmness preferred, as well as the areas that are most comfortable and calming. Even a brief hand or foot massage can promote calming and relaxation.

- *Play calming music* in the evening just to listen to together, or in the background of your evening routines.

- *Read books together.* An older child can read alone or listen to an audio book.

- *Engage your child in quiet activities such as puzzles, coloring, Play-Doh®,* or other projects that do not involve a high amount of physical activity. Choose things that are not frustrating or challenging for your child, as those kinds of activities will not promote calmness and relaxation. Regardless of your child's age, you may find it helpful to make a list of appropriate evening activities to choose from when the inevitable whining about wanting to play video games ensues!

Regardless of your child's age or functioning level, there are many quiet calming activities that can assist with settling down toward bedtime in the evening. Use those that work best for your child and family, with the goal of avoiding high amounts of physical movement and stimulating sensory input. Time spent developing calming activity routines is an investment in helping children get the sleep they need, while making bedtime easier for parents.

GAVIN'S STORY

Gavin was a very active four-year-old boy with autism who preferred highly physical activities throughout the day and evening. He struggled to fall asleep, and his parents would often spend hours trying to get him to settle down enough even to stay in bed. Gavin's father typically got home from work around 7:00 P.M., and would engage Gavin in active games such as throwing him up in the air to make him laugh, chasing him around the house, and wrestling together on the floor. While Gavin enjoyed these roughhouse activities, they were very stimulating for his system and would get him wound up right before bed. When parents tried to start getting him ready for bed around 8:00 P.M., Gavin was over-stimulated and had great difficulty calming down.

Eliminating sugary bedtime snacks, avoiding electronics for at least two hours before bed, and keeping a consistent bedtime routine made a difference.

I worked with Gavin's parents to make the two hours leading up to bed more calming; to see if that would make the bedtime routine easier for all of them. His mother started giving him a warm bath with lavender essential oil before his father got home from work. She would dry him with a towel using firm even pressure all over his body, and then help him get into his pajamas. They would sit on the couch with blankets, and look at picture books together until Gavin's father got home. Instead of roughhousing together, Gavin's father used pillows and blankets to provide firm soothing pressure on his body. They played calming instrumental music during this time, and would sometimes squeeze playdoh, play with sensory bins filled with rice, or do sticker books together.

When it was time to head to bed, Gavin was more calm and regulated; his parents no longer had to work so hard to settle him down to stay in bed. In addition to these calming activities, we used other strategies such as eliminating sugary bedtime snacks, avoiding electronics for at least two hours before bed, and keeping a consistent bedtime routine. His parents also learned how to stay calm when Gavin was upset and to use more supportive communication with him. All of these strategies set Gavin and his parents up for success at bedtime, and he fell asleep more quickly and stayed asleep better throughout the night.

▶ Key Take-Away

Calming activities in the hours leading up to bedtime help children settle down for sleep more quickly and easily.

Beware of Caffeine and Sugar Before Bed

What you eat impacts your functioning all through the day and night. This is obvious to anyone who has had a large caffeinated beverage late in the evening, and then lay in bed with eyes wide open and heart pounding while trying to fall asleep! Your child is impacted the same way. There are certain foods and ingredients that are not well suited for supporting sleep, and caffeine is certainly one of them. Beyond caffeine, foods containing simple carbs and sugars are also not supportive of sleep, as they cause an energy rush shortly after consumption. If your child has difficulty with sleep, it is wise to consider the role of food.

Energy drinks are particularly problematic where sleep is concerned.

The simplest rule where sleep is concerned is to avoid caffeine beyond early afternoon, as it can interfere with falling asleep at night. While some people are more sensitive to the altering quality of caffeine, it is usually alerting and not calming. Drinking or eating foods with caffeine in the later afternoon and evening can interfere with falling asleep at bedtime.

Energy drinks are particularly problematic where sleep is concerned, and this is something to be aware of with teens and young adults in particular as they tend to consume more of these items than younger children. These beverages not only have high amounts of caffeine, but also energy producing nutrients (ex: B vitamins) and herbs that increase alertness and nervous system activation. I would argue that these types of energy drinks are not appropriate regardless of sleep concerns, but they are certainly not helpful for people with sleep problems.

With regard to food and sleep, it is best to avoid feeding your child snacks containing sugar and simple processed carbohydrates, as these can interfere with falling asleep. Better options include whole grains, protein and healthy fats. Sleep-supportive snacks include options such as:

- Bananas
- Berries
- Whole grain toast with peanut or almond butter
- Hummus with veggies or whole grain chips
- Nuts such as almonds and walnuts
- Granola (with or without milk)
- Avocados (guacamole) with veggies or whole grain chips
- Fish
- Turkey or chicken
- Eggs
- Rice
- Beans

Some children do very well with a small protein shake before bed, especially when the protein powder is mixed with sleep supportive foods such as nuts, berries or bananas. Having a healthy snack before bed can be more supportive of sleep than going to bed on an empty stomach. However, eating a large portion of food right before bed can be counterproductive for sleep. Dinner should be the last large meal of the day, with the bedtime snack consisting of a smaller portion. If your child is having difficulty sleeping, then providing sleep-supportive snacks may be a helpful solution.

> ▶ **Key Take-Away**
>
> What your child eats and drinks before bed can make the difference between sleeping well and sleeping poorly. Provide a small sleep-supportive bedtime snack to help ensure a good night's sleep for everyone in the family.

Turn Off Screens

The light emitted by electronic screens fools the brain into thinking it's daylight, which makes it more difficult to fall asleep and stay asleep.

Did you know that spending time in the evening on the computer, video gaming systems, tablet, smart phone, or television negatively impacts sleep for children and adults? Research has repeatedly demonstrated that using electronics in the hours leading up to bedtime negatively impacts sleep onset and quality.[2] The consensus is that you should avoid screens for at least 45 minutes prior to trying to sleep, and some researchers recommend up to two hours of screen-free time before bed—and so should your children.

The light from these devices makes the brain think it is daytime. The result is that production of the hormone melatonin, which is needed for helping us get sleepier as bedtime approaches, is impeded. As the sun goes down the melatonin production should increase, allowing us to wind down and sleep when it's bedtime. Light from electronic gadgets such as televisions, laptops, tablets, and video games, tricks the brain into thinking it is daytime so as to reduce melatonin production.[3] The reduction in melatonin at night makes it more difficult for us to fall and stay asleep.

An additional problem is that these devices keep our mind and nervous system stimulated and engaged, which also makes sleep more difficult. While some people feel they are using the visual and auditory stimulation as a distractor to help them sleep, the reverse is actually true. Having these devices on close to bedtime makes it more difficult to fall asleep and negatively impacts the quality of our sleep throughout the night when left on.

> Children should not bring electronics into their rooms at night, as the temptation to surf the Internet, play games, respond to texts, and so on is difficult for children to regulate.

If your child is having any sleep-related difficulties, addressing screen time in the evenings is essential. Talk with your children about the negative impact of screens on sleep. Set new rules for times these devices can be used, and help children establish new evening routines that will better support their sleep.

Children should not bring electronics into their rooms at night, as the temptation to surf the Internet, play games, respond to texts, and so on is difficult for them to regulate. This is especially a problem for teenagers who may lose vital hours of sleep at night due to texting and social media use. These devices should have a home on the kitchen counter or other location in the house during the overnight period so they do not disrupt children's sleep.

It is important for parents to model this behavior as well by not using devices right up until bedtime, and not sleeping with devices right next to the bed. Simply reducing exposure to electronic screens near bedtime will improve sleep for the entire family.

VICTOR'S STORY

I had been working with Victor, age 10, and his parents for a year when they decided it was time to do something about his sleep issues. Victor had been diagnosed with ADHD, mood disorder, and anxiety and he had always struggled to fall asleep at night. When I first met him he was spending many hours each day on electronics, which was making him more irritable and dysregulated.

> The light from the screen reduced melatonin production, and kept his brain alert rather than in a drowsy state.

His parents had reduced his daytime electronics use to 90 minutes each day, but nighttime was a different story. They had put a television in his bedroom years earlier, as watching TV was the method they had used to get him to sleep at night. Victor would go to bed around 9:00 P.M. with the television on, and would generally fall asleep within an hour or two. If he woke up in the night he would continue watching TV, as it stayed on in his room all night long.

Victor was not getting enough sleep, and certainly wasn't getting good quality sleep. He was difficult to get going in the morning, and complained of fatigue almost every day. I explained to Victor and his parents that having the television on in his room all night was exacerbating his sleep problems. While it distracted him until he finally couldn't keep his eyes open any longer, it was also keeping him stimulated and making it more difficult to wind down to sleep. The light from the screen reduced melatonin production, and kept his brain alert rather than in a drowsy state. The noise and action was also stimulating and counterproductive to sleep.

His parents decided to remove the television from Victor's bedroom and we implemented a plan to support his sleep. His plan involved changing bedtime routines, incorporating more calming activities prior to bedtime, avoiding screen time for two hours leading up to bed, and using supplements to help him fall asleep faster and stay asleep longer. Victor was convinced it would be impossible for him to go to bed without TV, but the new strategies helped him fall asleep more quickly and that made the adjustment smoother. Within days Victor was sleeping longer and more soundly, was easier to wake in the morning, and his overall mood improved. Removing the television from his room was key to supporting healthy sleep habits and reducing his overall symptoms.

Key Take-Away

Reducing exposure to electronic devices—screen time—in the hour leading up to bedtime reduces the time needed to fall asleep, and improves sleep quality.

CHAPTER 10

SLEEP STRATEGIES

It is an important developmental milestone
for children to learn how to fall asleep
without a parent at night.

If you've ever experienced sleeping on an uncomfortable bed, or in a noisy hotel room, or with blankets that were too warm, you know the impact that physical environment has on sleep. Sensory aspects of the environment—including smells, temperature, bedding, and light—all play a role in supporting or detracting from sleep. Below are several guiding principles to keep in mind when creating a sleep-supportive environment for children:

- *Make sure your child's bed, pillows, and sheets/blankets are comfortable **according to your child's preferences.*** Some children have sensitive sensory systems, and may struggle to sleep if the texture of bedding is uncomfortable to them. Allow your child to experiment with what feels most comfortable, even if it's not what you would choose.

- *Some children benefit from the deep pressure provided by heavy comforters and pillows.* Weighted blankets can be purchased to place over the child at night in order to soothe the sensory system and support better sleep. Sleeping bags can also provide sensory support and a feeling of security. Lycra® bed sheets are very firm and stretchy, and can provide some children with the firm pressure and support needed to promote sleep.

- *Place furniture in a configuration in the room that is supportive for sleep.* This may mean having the bed away from the door so light doesn't shine into the room if the door is left open. Clocks or other devices with lights on them should be dimmed or kept away from the head of the bed. Many children prefer the security of having their bed up against a wall, as opposed to having open space on both sides of the bed.

- *A bed tent can help some children feel more secure and comfortable at night.* Such tents fit over the mattress and provide an enclosed space for sleeping. This can be especially helpful for children with night fears, or whose sensory systems are averse to open spaces.

- *Cooler temperatures are better for sleeping,* as research has shown that elevated core body temperature makes it harder to fall asleep at night, and more difficult to wake up in the morning.[1]

- *The presence of noise in the sleep environment* can make it more difficult to initiate and maintain sleep. Use of white noise machines, fans, or other devices that emit low-level continuous noise can raise the auditory disruption threshold and allow people to fall asleep faster and stay asleep longer.[2] Playing calming instrumental music can also be a useful auditory strategy. It is best to set the music to repeat continuously throughout the night, as that makes it easier to fall back asleep if your child is awakened in the night.

- *Smells present in the sleep environment can support or inhibit sleep.* Research has shown that aromatherapy, particularly the scent of lavender, allows for deeper sleep and a more alert state upon waking.[3]

- *Children with allergies,* particularly those involving congestion due to mold, dust mites and pollen, may face additional environmental barriers to quality sleep. Regular washing of bedding and pillows in hot water can help, in addition to the use of covers that seal mattresses and pillows from potential allergens. Use of an air purifier may also be beneficial for both allergen reduction and noise filtering.

- *Managing light exposure is also critical for optimum sleep.* Exposure to light that is in alignment with natural cycles of sunlight and darkness help regulate melatonin production and overall sleep cycles. Exposure to increasing darkness before sleep helps with initiation of sleep at bedtime. Increasing light exposure in the hour leading to waking helps reduce melatonin production and makes it easier to wake in an alert state. Using strategies such as gradually reducing the amount of overhead light exposure in the hours leading up to sleep makes it easier to fall asleep. Room-darkening curtains can be helpful to ensure longer sleep duration in the morning hours.

• *Remove televisions, gaming systems, smartphones,* and other electronic devices from the sleep environment, as they inhibit quality sleep.

BROOKE'S STORY

Brooke, age 14, had struggled with anxiety for as long as she could remember. Nighttime was the worst, as she was constantly startled by sounds in the house and felt physically uncomfortable in her bedroom. She would try to leave her television on all night long to distract her until she was so tired, she finally fell asleep. Even though she was a teenager, she would often sneak into her parents' room to sleep on the floor since she felt more comfortable in their bedroom. Her level of discomfort in her bedroom was causing her to have very poor sleep, which was causing her overall level of anxiety to worsen.

She and I discussed what she liked and disliked about her bedroom, and identified specific things that were causing problems for her sleep. She knew that the noises in the house were causing a major problem, so we tried a white noise machine and soothing music to block other sounds. Brooke also felt nervous having her bed sticking out into the center of the room, so she and her parents moved furniture around so her bed could be against one wall of her room. This helped her feel more secure.

She experimented with different kinds of bedding her parents had in the house, and found that sleeping with multiple pillows and soft comforters helped her sleep better. An essential oil diffuser with lavender oil also proved to be a comforting and sleep-supportive strategy for her. The television was removed from her room, and her parents required that she leave her cell phone outside of her bedroom at night.

These environmental supports proved helpful for Brooke, and allowed the cognitive behavior strategies she was learning to work more effectively. She also benefitted from some targeted supplements and diet changes to support her sleep as well. Improving the physical comfort of her room was a simple strategy that allowed the other approaches to work more effectively.

> **Key Take-Away**
> The physical environment can support or prevent quality sleep. Creating an optimal sleep environment for your child can be a simple solution to better sleep.

Helping Children Sleep on Their Own

If you are the parent of a child who is unable to fall asleep on his or her own, you know how frustrating that can be for all involved. It is easy for parents to fall into the routine of sleeping with children, or at least staying with them until they fall asleep, in order to get them to go to sleep and stay asleep during the night. This is problematic for both the child and the parent—neither gets a good night's sleep! It is an important developmental milestone for children to learn how to fall asleep without a parent at night, and to be able to get themselves back to sleep if they awaken in the night.

You may have a child who insists that you stay in the room with them while they fall asleep, or even all through the night. Or you may be in a situation where your child is used to falling asleep in your bed, and possibly staying in bed with you all night. Either way, the end goal should be that you are able to put your child to bed and leave, and that your child is able to fall asleep and stay asleep through the night. There is a systematic process you can use to successfully address this issue regardless of your child's age or functioning level. While it may take many weeks to accomplish, the end result of your child being able to fall asleep on his or her own is well worth the effort!

The first step in the process is to determine your starting point, which is essentially what your child is currently comfortable with. If you typically lay down in bed with your child when s/he falls asleep, then that is the starting point. The goal is to systematically move yourself further from your child, and out of the room over time. The first night you may sit on the edge of the bed while rubbing your child's back.

The next step might be to sit in a chair right next to the bed while you give your child a back rub. Each night you can move the chair slightly further from your child's bed. When you get to the point where you are close to the door, make the transition to sitting right outside the door. From that point your child may be falling asleep easily without you.

If your child is still concerned about where you are, you can continue the process of moving yourself further from the bedroom door into other rooms/parts of the house. Some parents find it helpful to institute a schedule of "checks" to assure the child they will be in to check on them every so often in the hour after putting them to bed.

Children deserve the opportunity to reach the developmental milestone of being able to fall asleep and stay asleep on their own, as this is a critical component of cognitive growth, development of self-regulation, and personal competence.

The speed with which you can implement this plan depends on your child's anxiety level, temperament, and ability to manage change. It also depends on your ability as a parent to manage your own anxiety about the process. A highly anxious child who struggles greatly with change may need a slower progression from one step to the next as you work your way out of the room. Other children do fine with parents moving themselves out of the room more quickly.

If your child becomes highly upset and dysregulated at any point in the process, simply go back to the last step that was working well and make a smaller change. For example, if transitioning from sitting next to your child on the bed to sitting on a chair next to their bed is highly upsetting, then go back to sitting on the bed for one night. The next night you may move a little bit further down the edge of the bed instead of moving into a chair.

You are looking for steps that move away from the current pattern, but at a pace that does not provoke high anxiety for your child. However, it is also important to recognize that your child may be somewhat uncomfortable with this entire process, and that is okay. He may verbalize that he just wants you to keep things the same, may try to convince you he cannot fall asleep any other way, or may even cry about the changes.

This is all to be expected, as your child genuinely does perceive that he will never be able to sleep on his own. You can continue to offer reassurance that this is something he can do, and that you will continue to help. If your child is uncomfortable to the point of having a massive temper tantrum, screaming for long periods of time, or otherwise becoming completely dysregulated, then it is important to take this process very slowly so your child acclimates to very tiny adjustments on the path to making bigger changes.

It may take you many weeks to transition out of the room so that your child learns to fall asleep independently, but it is definitely better than staying in the room and preventing the development of this important skill.

You can use this same process if your child is used to sleeping in your room with you. Instead of you moving farther from the child, you are going to use the same process to systematically move the child further from you. The first step may be to place a sleeping bag, air mattress, or other sleeping item on the floor next to your bed and have your child sleep there. Then you can systematically move the child's sleeping surface further from you toward the door, and then eventually into the hallway and into his bedroom. I have found that for many families it is easier to remove themselves from the child's room than remove the child from their room, but it definitely can work either way, depending on what the current pattern is.

If your child wakes up in the night and is unable to fall back to sleep by themselves, put the child back in bed and repeat the process of situating yourself wherever you were at the start of bedtime. Avoid the impulse to just put the child in bed with you, or go back to old habits because it feels easier in the moment. This process takes perseverance on the part of the parent to implement and stick to new patterns.

While it may seem exhausting to consider working through the process of helping your child fall asleep and stay asleep without you, it is far less exhausting than spending every night jumping through hoops to get your child to sleep. Parents need and deserve to have time to themselves in the evenings, and to get a good night's sleep. Children also deserve the opportunity to reach the developmental milestone of being able to fall asleep and stay asleep on their own, as this is a critical component of cognitive growth, development of self-regulation, and personal competence. Time and effort spent on this process now will save much frustration and lost sleep in the long term.

> **► Key Take-Away**
> It is important for children to learn to fall asleep and stay asleep on their own at night. There is a systematic process for moving your child to greater independence with falling asleep, and the time and effort spent on it will save years of frustration and poor sleep.

Supplements for Sleep Support

Even with other strategies in place, some children need additional interventions to achieve a healthy amount and quality of sleep. This is where specific sleep-supportive nutritional supplements can play an important role in a treatment plan. There are numerous research-based nutrient and herbal supplements that can safely and effectively improve sleep issues. Consultation with your child's health care provider(s) is recommended when considering supplement supports. This is especially the case if your child is taking prescription medications, in order to avoid potentially negative drug-supplement interactions.

Below are some of the more common supplement supports for sleep:

- *Melatonin* – This is the hormone our body makes that helps us wind down to fall asleep when it gets dark. Supplementing with melatonin can help with falling asleep, and dosing for children generally starts at 0.5-1mg and can increase from there. There are also extended release melatonin formulas that can be helpful to support falling asleep and staying asleep through the night. Research has shown that melatonin is safe for children to use in the short and longer terms.[4] Many children may benefit from melatonin for a period of time, and then do not need it nightly once their sleep cycles become better regulated and other sleep-supportive strategies are implemented.

- *Magnesium* – This mineral supports brain and body relaxation, and can be especially helpful for children who experience restless legs/body, muscle tension, and anxious thoughts at night. Eating foods with more magnesium can help (ex: dark leafy greens, seeds, and nuts) as can taking supplemental magnesium in powder or capsule form. There are also powder formulations that can be mixed into beverages for easy dosing with children. An Epsom salt bath before bed can also be calming and allow magnesium to be absorbed via the skin.

- *Valerian/lemon balm* – Research has shown that this blend of herbs can induce calming and relaxation, especially for children who tend toward hyperactivity and have a difficult time settling down at night.[5] It can be found in tea form as well as liquid and capsule formulations. Valerian can also be used in isolation as a calming and sedating herb.

- *Chamomile* – This is another herb that can support calming and relaxation, and can be given as a tea drink or in a liquid or capsule form. There are also essential oil formulations containing chamomile, which can be used topically or diffused into the air to support sleep.

- *Tryptophan* – This amino acid is commonly associated with eating turkey, although you would need to eat a lot of turkey to experience drowsiness! Tryptophan supports serotonin production which promotes calming in the brain. It can be found in capsule and powder forms, and is often combined with other nutrients in sleep-supportive supplement blends.

- *Vitamin B6* – This vitamin is known for supporting sleep in multiple ways. It is a critical component of the biochemical pathway needed for melatonin and serotonin production. There is also evidence that B6 can support proper dream states, and may be helpful at reducing nightmares. Using appropriate doses of B6 in the morning may be more beneficial than when taken at night, as some people find that B6 is over-activating in the evening and makes it harder for them to fall asleep.

Specific nutrient and herbal supplements can be simple solutions to childhood sleep challenges. They are often most beneficial when combined with environmental and behavioral supports, and can make other approaches work more effectively. If your child is struggling to get enough quality sleep, it is definitely worth exploring whether supplements containing targeted nutrients and/or herbs may be part of the solution.

AMY'S STORY

Amy was five years old when her parents brought her to see me. She had been diagnosed with ADHD, anxiety, oppositional-defiance disorder, and speech delay. Her parents were extremely frustrated, as they had taken Amy to numerous types of therapists.

She was taking four medications; and she was still not sleeping well, and having significant behavioral dysregulation at home. Amy had been adopted as a baby, and had struggled with multiple aspects of development since that time.

All of these solutions improved Amy's sleep, but she was still struggling to consistently fall asleep easily at night.

It was clear to me that one of the primary issues impacting Amy's symptoms was poor sleep. Not only was she not getting nearly enough hours of sleep each night, but her sleep was disrupted by frequent night waking. She had been prescribed three different medications to get her to sleep; yet none were working effectively, and they all carried risks of significant side effects. I referred Amy to a sleep medicine physician for consultation, as she had many red flags indicating that she was having sleep apnea or other diagnosable sleep problems. A sleep study determined that she was having sleep apnea, and she subsequently had her tonsils and adenoids removed.

We worked with the parents to develop consistent calming evening routines to support Amy to settle down before bed. They also instituted restrictions on screen time, and removed access to the television and tablet during the night. All of these solutions improved Amy's sleep, but she was still struggling to consistently fall asleep easily at night. A combination of melatonin and valerian, approved by her physician, provided the additional support she needed to fall asleep quickly at bedtime.

This combination of strategies, including sleep-supporting supplements, allowed Amy to achieve a healthy duration and quality of sleep each night without the use of prescription sleep-aids.

This, in turn, led to improvements in her behavior and functioning during the day.

> **Key Take-Away**
> Using specific supplements at the proper doses can help children fall asleep, stay asleep, and have good quality sleep at night, without the side effect risks of prescription medications.

part four: **movement**

CHAPTER 11

MOVEMENT
IS ESSENTIAL

Minimal movement creates negative
consequences for bodies and brains.

Movement is critical for building healthy brains and bodies. Research continues to demonstrate the many benefits of movement and exercise for preventing and treating a wide range of physical and mental health conditions.[1] Physical activity improves our mood, helps us think more clearly, and sharpens our mental focus. Muscle movement activates the neurochemical system in our brain to keep brain connections active and flexible. Physical activity also stimulates the growth of connections between cells in the brain, allowing for an increase in overall connectivity between and within regions of the brain.

While movement is essential for optimal health in all age groups, it is especially critical for children. Physical movement is necessary not only for motor development, but also for sensory, cognitive, emotional, and social development. When children's need for movement is unmet, problems can occur in many areas.[2] If your child is struggling with inattention, anxiety, mood dysregulation, hyperactivity, learning disorders, sensory processing or challenging behaviors, then movement is a necessary component to consider in improving function.

With so much technology available today, everyone tends to spend more time sitting than moving—and this is especially true for children. This has negative consequences for our bodies and brains. While regularly scheduled exercise is great, you do not have to engage in vigorous exercise every day to get the benefits of physical movement. Even simple activities like walking or stretching are supportive of brain health and development.

The goal is to find ways to help children move throughout the day to support their development and behavioral regulation. Participating in activities such as team sports, dance classes, and swim lessons are certainly excellent options for movement. However, some children are not able to participate in these kinds of formal exercise opportunities. Even children who do participate in organized sports or lessons will benefit from a variety of movement opportunities throughout the day.

If your child is struggling with inattention, anxiety, mood dysregulation, hyperactivity, learning disorders, sensory processing or challenging behaviors, then movement is a necessary component to consider in improving function.

Some of you may be thinking that your child never seems to stop moving! Children who tend to be hyperactive or constantly seek out movement need structured physical activities to support proper development and regulation. Many children with the challenges discussed in this book have underlying brain-body connections that are lacking, and there are specific interventions that can help these children develop the connections needed for symptom reduction. This section will provide suggestions and strategies to help your child engage in the kinds of movement activities that will support his development and improve functioning across the board.

Reduce Screen Time

The amount of time children and adults spend engaged in sedentary activities has skyrocketed as the amount of technology has increased. Children today spend a significant amount of time each day engaged in "screen time" activities that reduce physical movement and promote disengagement from the world around them.[3]

Research has shown that as the amount of time in front of screens increases, so does the risk of learning, attention, emotional and behavior problems for children.[4] Screen time has a negative effect on mood and behavior, and many parents notice a significant difference in their child's temperament, communication, attitude, and behavior following lengthy periods of time spent on video games or other screen time activities.

There are clearly many reasons to be concerned about your child spending an excessive amount of time in front of screens, and reduction in physical movement throughout the day is one of them.

> As the amount of time in front of screens increases, so does the risk of learning, attention, emotional and behavior problems for children.

One of the best ways to ensure that children get the physical movement their brains and bodies need is to reduce the amount of time spent on screen time activities including television, computers, smart phones, tablets, video games, and DVD players. All of these devices promote a sedentary lifestyle, and detract from time spent engaged in healthy movement. While some time spent on electronic devices is not harmful, it must be done in moderation.

The American Academy of Pediatrics has recommended that children under the age of two should not be engaged in screen time of any sort. Past the age of two, the recommendation is that children be exposed to no more than two hours of screen time per day.[5]

The reality is that most children I have seen over the course of my professional career are spending far more than two hours a day in front of screens. Between the time spent on the computer and tablets at school, video games at home, smart phones while at the grocery store, and DVD players in the car, the average eight-year-old child spends eight hours in front of screens daily. The numbers are higher for teenagers—often 10 hours or more each day. These statistics are certainly cause for concern, particularly where the movement needs of children are concerned.

Children may complain about not having unlimited access to electronic devices; but they certainly can and should find other activities to occupy their time.

One of the simplest solutions to ensure children move more is to reduce the amount of screen time they have each day. I encourage parents to set limits for two hours of screen time at home each day at most. It is unfortunate that more schools are opting to sit children in front of screens for longer periods each day, and I recognize that parents have limited control over the time their children are exposed to electronic devices at school. Parents can control this at home, however, and should monitor device use to ensure children are not spending excessive amounts of time in front of screens.

Some parents may be concerned that their children won't have anything to do, or that they will have to figure out how to entertain their children when they are not engaged in screen time. Children may complain about not having unlimited access to electronic devices; but they certainly can and should find other activities to occupy their time. Parents can provide a list of other activities for children to choose from, or can simply allow kids to "be bored" if they do not select other things to do. Time spent sitting with "nothing to do" is healthier for the brain and body than time sitting absorbed in passive electronic stimulation!

Parents may also worry that restricting time spent on electronic devices may put their child at a social disadvantage, as many children connect with each other via social media, texting, and online video games. I can assure parents that enforcing limits on time spent on devices will not have a detrimental impact on their child's social engagement. In fact, the opposite is likely true.

Children learn valuable communication and social interaction skills when engaged in real life interactions with other human beings, as opposed to interacting with others via devices. Children and teenagers can absolutely have friends, engage in social activities, and develop appropriate relational skills without constant access to screens.[6]

From a movement standpoint, reducing time spent on electronic devices promotes more physical activity. Reducing time spent on devices, even if for specific periods of time each day, will increase movement throughout the day. It frees up time for children to participate in active games, household chores, sports, and other tasks that provide valuable opportunities for physical activity. The simplest solution to the problem of overly sedentary lifestyles for children is to limit the amount of screen time daily.

Parents should be prepared to model moderation of screen time for their children, as it is futile to tell children to find other things to do with their time when they see their parent constantly absorbed in sedentary screen time.

Upon learning the recommendations for limiting screen time, some parents decide to put limits in place for their children. Others may feel overwhelmed at the thought of drastically reducing screen time all at once. For these parents it is likely best to look for ways to gradually reduce screen time so as to increase engagement in other activities. Starting points may include not allowing use of phones and other devices during mealtimes, not playing DVDs or allowing children to play with smart phones on brief car trips, or removing televisions from children's bedrooms.

Gradually reduce the amount of time children are allowed to engage with a screen, and at the same time gradually increase the time they are expected to engage in other activities—especially those that involve physical movement. The time and energy spent on helping children moderate their engagement in screen time is well worth the beneficial outcomes of improved physical and mental health.

JACOB'S STORY

Like many teenagers, Jacob preferred to spend as much time as possible playing video games, surfing the web, texting people, watching television, and perusing social media websites. His parents were frustrated with his constant "bad attitude," resistance to doing what he was asked to do at home, and poor performance in school. Jacob had been diagnosed with ADHD when he was in elementary school, and had a lengthy history of irritable mood, poor frustration tolerance, and difficulties in school.

When I consulted with his parents, they wanted to know what they could do to better support him as his difficulties seemed to be getting worse instead of better with age. One of the things I asked them to do was determine how much time, on average, Jacob was spending in front of screens each day. They estimated that it was around five hours, but were stunned to discover that their son was easily spending nine hours a day on screen time during the week—and more on weekends. When we discussed limiting his screen time, however, they were both concerned that he would be "socially disconnected," and weren't convinced that something as simple as reducing screen time could actually improve his mood and behavior.

> He complained bitterly about being bored, having nothing to do, and how unfair the new rules were.

I challenged them to do an experiment and reduce screen time to no more than three hours a day for one week. They were willing to try it, so I talked with Jacob about the problems with excessive screen time and how it might be connected to the difficulties he was having. I met with him and his parents together to discuss the new rules for screen time at home and his parents implemented the plan the next day.

When I met with them the following week, the parents were pleased to report that they had noticed a difference in Jacob's mood and behavior over the prior few days. Initially he was resistive to following the new rules, and angry with his parents for enforcing them. He complained bitterly about being bored, having nothing to do, and how unfair the new rules were.

After a few days, he began to start engaging with activities he had previously enjoyed such as building with Legos, drawing, and shooting hoops outside. His mood brightened noticeably, and he was less sullen and resistive to doing things his parents requested of him. At our appointment, Jacob himself admitted that he felt somewhat happier and had rediscovered how much he enjoyed some of his hobbies.

The small changes over the course of the week's experiment were enough to convince his parents that excessive screen time was exacerbating Jacob's difficulties. They continued to implement the screen time restrictions, and the benefits continued as well. There were many other strategies implemented to support symptoms improvement for Jacob, but reduced screen time was an important initial step.

▶ **Key Take-Away**

Reducing the amount of time children spend on screen time activities supports improved mood, learning, social development, and behavior. Less time spent with electronic devices allows for increased time spent on movement activities, which benefits both physical and mental health.

CHAPTER 12

MOVEMENT ACTIVITIES THROUGHOUT THE DAY

Get creative and see how many movement opportunities you can come up with by having your child help you.

As a parent, you are likely running around getting in bits of movement throughout the day doing chores and various household activities; so why not get your children in on the action? Chores not only get kids moving, but they also build skills for independence and help develop a sense of personal competence. Everyone in the family can play a role in contributing to maintenance of the home—even very young or impaired children. As they get older and more competent, children can carry out some of these responsibilities on their own while younger or more impaired children can be a helper to parents engaging in these tasks.

Household chores can provide structured purposeful movement that promotes sensory integration, develops motor skills, enhances problem-solving skills, improves frustration tolerance, and encourages a healthy sense of personal competence. Here is a sampling of chore activities to consider for your child:

- *Laundry* – There are many roles within the laundry process can provide movement and learning opportunities. Sorting laundry from one container to another provides predictable rhythmic movement. Carrying baskets of laundry, or pushing/ pulling them, provides the deep pressure input some children crave and can be very calming and regulating. Moving laundry from basket to washer, or from washer to dryer, also provides rhythmic regulating movement. Putting clothes away in drawers and closets also allows for organized movement and motor control.

- *Wiping surfaces* – Children can learn to clean surfaces such as tables, chairs, counters, windows, mirrors, floors, and sinks with a wet or dry cloth. This encourages large and small muscle movement, along with providing deep pressure input many children crave. The movements involved in these tasks are predictable and regulating, and integrate many aspects of sensation with muscle activity.

  If you have wood or tile floors, you can have your child stand on cleaning cloths and move around the floor to wipe them down. It is a little like skating, which works on motor control and balance in a fun way. If your house is like most that have children living in them, you have no shortage of surfaces to wipe down each day—so get your child moving to help!

- *Raking and shoveling* – If you live in a climate with four seasons, there are many opportunities throughout the year for raking leaves and shoveling snow. These tasks incorporate the heavy muscle work that can be calming and regulating for children. They are also structured and purposeful, and don't require great precision.

- *Vacuuming* – Pushing and pulling the vacuum around the house gets kids up on their feet, and moving throughout the house. This also provides deep regulating input to the sensory system, while working on motor control and problem solving to maneuver around furniture and other objects. If your child is sensitive to loud noises, you can try headphones or ear plugs to make an activity like this more tolerable.

- *Taking out the garbage* – Trash removal needs to be done regularly, and is a simple way for your child to help and move at the same time. Gathering the various trash baskets from around the house is one way to provide movement. Your child can help dump the various containers into one bag, and then take the trash out to the main container outdoors. Younger children can help a parent wheel the trash bin to the street as needed, while older children can learn to walk it down on their own.

- *Putting away groceries* – This is another opportunity for your child to get deep pressure input while building muscle strength and coordination. Have your children help carry bags of groceries in from the car, as well as assist with putting items away in the kitchen and throughout the home.

- *Walking the dog* – If your family has a dog or other pets, chances are someone needs to take the dog out for a walk or play with the other pets on a regular basis. This is an excellent opportunity for your child to engage in movement while also being in a helping role. Some children may be able to walk the dog or play with pets on their own, while others may go with a parent or other family member. This is a simple way to build in healthy movement each day.

Hopefully the above ideas will start you thinking about all the ways you can encourage your child to move by helping out around the house. Everyone in the family can contribute to household chores and necessary activities in some way, big or small. The benefits of involving your child in these tasks are many, and they provide brief but meaningful opportunities for structured physical movement throughout the day.

Get creative and see how many movement opportunities you can come up with on a daily or weekly basis just by having your child help with the things you are already doing around the house.

▶ **Key Take-Away**

Household chores can provide structured purposeful movement that promotes sensory integration, develops motor skills, enhances problem-solving skills, improves frustration tolerance, and encourages a healthy sense of personal competence.

Active Games

Games involving physical movement can be a great way to spend quality time together as a family while also providing exercise. Active games allow children to gain muscle strength, motor coordination, integrate movement and sensation, and balance control. Beyond the physical benefits, these kinds of games provide opportunities for kids to improve learning, social skills, communication, frustration tolerance, and behavioral regulation.

> Active games allow children to gain muscle strength, motor coordination, integrate movement and sensation, and balance control.

Below is a list of indoor and outdoor games that will get your kids moving. Some of these require multiple people and can be done as a family, while others are movement activities your child can engage in independently:

- Freeze tag
- Relay races
- Wrestling
- Red Light - Green Light
- Hopscotch
- Beanbag toss
- Hula Hoops
- Dancing to various types of music
- Simon Says
- Musical chairs
- What time is it, Mr. Fox?
- Four Square
- Frisbee
- Catch
- Shooting hoops

- Horse shoes
- Charades
- Balloon volleyball
- Animal walks (bear, crab, snake, etc.)
- Sack Races
- Corn Hole

Some parents find it helpful to keep a list of active games handy for times when no one can come up with ideas of what to do. This can be especially helpful when children are told to "go play," yet can't seem to find anything to occupy their time. Simply show them the list of options they can choose from if they don't want to come up with their own ideas. Keep adding to the list over time as children grow and learn new games.

▶ **Key Take-Away**
Games involving physical activity are great for encouraging physical movement and building family relationships.

Obstacle Courses

Obstacle courses are an excellent way to provide organized movement indoors or outdoors. An obstacle course consists of a series of physical movements/activities done in a circuit. Components of an obstacle course can include the following types of movements and activities:

- Jump into a pile of pillows
- Roll over an exercise ball

- Do 10 jumping jacks
- Toss beanbags into a bucket
- Crawl through a fabric tunnel
- Sit on a scooter board, and use your arms to push across the floor
- Jump on a mini trampoline
- Walk across a tape line on the floor
- Jump into and out of hoola hoops
- Walk and balance something on your head
- Crawl under a blanket suspended between two chairs
- Stand in a pillow case and jump across the floor
- Jump backward on squares of paper
- Slither on your stomach from one spot to another
- Walk while trying to keep a cotton ball or other small object on a spoon

There are many developmental benefits to having children engage in obstacle courses. They allow for structured movement, as opposed to the chaotic movement many children with hyperactivity and other challenges tend to seek out. Structured movement allows for appropriate sensory integration, development of motor coordination, and better emotional and behavioral regulation.

Obstacle courses also help children work on sequencing and memory, as each time they move through the course they need to recall what they need to do. Depending on the activities you include in the course, children have the opportunity to experience a variety of sensory inputs such as bouncing, moving backward, swinging, falling, and spinning. They also can work on balance and motor control, as well as improving muscle strength and the ability to plan movements needed for various activities.

Structured movement allows for appropriate sensory integration, development of motor coordination, and better emotional and behavioral regulation.

Obstacle courses are very flexible in that they can be easily tailored to the age and ability level of the child. Even with multiple children participating, the activities can be modified to meet the needs and coordination abilities of each child. The obstacle course can be kept the same or changed for variety as often as desired. Older children can participate in developing the activities and sequence for the course. These activities can be done with parent supervision/support, or children can attempt them independently. See what ideas you can come up with to create movement-rich obstacle courses for your child and family!

▶ Key Take-Away

Obstacle courses are simple to create, can be used with children of all ages and developmental levels, and provide opportunities for structured movement indoors and outdoors.

CHAPTER 13

MOVEMENT STRATEGIES

The stretch and sturdiness of Lycra
allows kids to climb, swing, push, pull,
and bounce in a contained space.

I f the word Lycra conjures up images of bike shorts or bad outfits from the 1980s, you may be wondering why on earth there would be anything about such a strange fabric in a book about children with attention, anxiety, mood, and behavior challenges. It turns out that Lycra (also known as Spandex), that soft stretchy synthetic fabric typically used in athletic-type clothing, is an exceptionally versatile tool for encouraging therapeutic movement in children.

Good quality Lycra provides enough resistance that children experience a firm comfortable pressure when they push against it, which provides calming input to the brain and body. The stretch and sturdiness of the fabric allows kids to climb, swing, push, pull, and bounce in a contained space depending on how you use the Lycra. It provides a valuable movement opportunity in any environment, and there are even some portable options. In addition to the movement benefits, Lycra can provide a very calming sensory environment that is useful for reducing anxiety and improving emotional and behavioral regulation.

It turns out that Lycra (also known as Spandex), that soft stretchy synthetic fabric typically used in athletic-type clothing, is an exceptionally versatile tool for encouraging therapeutic movement in children.

Here are some ways to use Lycra with children of all ages to promote organized movement and sensory input:

- *Lycra Body Socks* – These are essentially large rectangular bags made by sewing two pieces of Lycra fabric together, and cutting a hole down the middle of one side to allow the child to climb into the bag. Body socks provide a contained space for the child to move around or lie still. When they move their body against the bag they feel the calming pressure and resistance from the fabric. They also provide a welcome space away from environmental stimulation that may be overwhelming to the child. The Lycra allows light in, but permits the child to escape visual stimulation. Body socks are portable, and make a great tool to use at home, school, on vacation or anywhere else they may be beneficial for the child.

- *Lycra Chair Bands* – Tie a strip of Lycra fabric across the front legs of a chair so your child can fidget by kicking against the band. This is a great tool for children who struggle to sit still in a chair, or who benefit from movement while reading, doing homework, of even eating at the table. Kids can move their feet and legs against the band to experience the organizing pressure and movement, and it doesn't make any noise.

• *Lycra Movement Bands* – Cut wide strips of Lycra fabric in varying lengths to use for various purposes. An adult can hold one end of the strip while the child pulls on the other end for a "tug of war" style activity. You can also sew the two ends together to make a circle. Have your child sit or lie down with legs stretched out, and place one end of the circle around their feet and pull the other end around their head, shoulders or back. This provides great full-body pressure, and allows them to experiment with movement against the resistance of the band. These bands are also easy to use in many different environments, and are ideal for situations where your child needs movement but also needs to stay quiet.

• *Lycra Hammocks* – There are a variety of ways to use Lycra for hammocks. If you already have a hammock stand or hooks for an outdoor hammock, you can simply tie the ends of a long piece of Lycra to carabiner clips and then hook the carabiners onto your existing stand or hammock hooks.

If you don't have an existing stand or hooks, you can drill hooks into the ceiling indoors or on wooden posts/trees outdoors in order to hang your Lycra attached to the carabiner clips. Everyone in the family will enjoy the soft, supportive, even pressure that Lycra provides when you lie down in the hammock. Lycra also allows you to easily swing or bounce your child in the hammock, which provides additional movement opportunities.

- *Lycra Swings* – A Lycra swing is similar to a hammock, except you need just one hook to hang it from the ceiling. Tie all four ends of the fabric piece to a carabiner clip or multiple clips, and then clip them all to the ceiling hook. You end up with a cocoon-type swing that allows your child to climb in and feel enveloped by the fabric while sitting, swinging or bouncing.

There are many ways to use Lycra fabric to create valuable movement opportunities for your child. While there are catalogs and companies online that carry equipment and therapeutic tools made from Lycra, the above ideas give you options for creating your own. Make sure you purchase high quality Lycra fabric to ensure durability.

DAMIEN'S STORY

Damien was an eight-year-old boy with a history of learning, mood, communication, and behavior challenges. He was one of those children with a host of symptoms, none of which fit neatly into a particular diagnostic category. Damien was born quite prematurely, and had struggled with a variety of health issues early in life. Intellectually he was very bright, but he struggled to manage his emotions and behaviors at school and home.

On his second visit to our clinic, I took Damien to the sensory gym to explore the equipment. He was very hyperactive and random with his movement, and had difficulty focusing long enough to follow even simple directions. I wanted to see if spending time in the Lycra hammock would provide calm and organizing movement input to his brain and body. He struggled initially to plan the movements needed to climb into the hammock, but was able to do so with my help.

> He was relaxed, calm, and engaged with me throughout the time he was in the Lycra hammock.

Once in the suspended Lycra, his body relaxed and he calmed almost immediately. The material enveloped him, and as he moved against it he experienced the sensation of comfortable pressure to his body. I gently swung the hammock to provide another movement experience, and then switched to a bouncing motion. Damien was relaxed, calm, and engaged with me throughout the time he was in the Lycra hammock. After multiple visits, he was able to plan the motor movements needed to climb into the hammock on his own, and then worked up to being able to climb up to the multiple higher layers of the hammock.

His parents were so encouraged by the changes they saw in him during and following his time in the Lycra that they purchased some Lycra to create their own hammock for Damien at home. They hung it in a corner of the family room, and it provided a valuable option for Damien to access calming movement at home. We also used a Lycra body sock with Damien at home and school, and that was another excellent and convenient option for giving him the type of movement he needed to organize his body and brain in both environments.

▶ **Key Take-Away**

Lycra fabric can provide movement benefits as well as a very calming sensory environment useful for reducing anxiety and improving emotional and behavioral regulation.

Reflex Integration

It is likely that you have never heard of reflex integration, yet it is a foundational issue for many of the children impacted by attention, anxiety, mood, and behavior challenges. You may be familiar with sensory integration, which is the brain's ability to make sense of and use information coming from the sensory environment. However, reflex integration forms a foundation for sensory integration and many other aspects of functioning. Integrating reflexes is necessary for appropriate learning, emotional control, impulse management, sensory integration, toileting skills, and motor skills development. Unintegrated reflexes can be involved in many of the symptoms experienced by children with attention, anxiety, mood, and behavior challenges.[1]

So what is a reflex? Reflexes are automatic actions the body takes in response to specific stimuli. Blinking is one example of a reflex. Another classic example is when your physician taps your knee during a physical exam, and your knee jumps a little. This is an automatic reflex in that you are not consciously thinking about your response—your body just does it. Reflexes such as these are meant to stay with us throughout our entire lives. In addition, there are also primitive reflexes that are meant to stay with us for a brief period of time, typically infancy, until they integrate and disappear. This happens because the brain and body mature and integrate those reflexes into higher-level functions.

Children with retained reflexes are literally stuck in a pattern of immature and simplistic neurological responses.

When the reflexes that should integrate do not, they are referred to as retained reflexes. These retained reflexes can interfere with higher-level functions and cause inefficiencies in the ways the brain handles input. They essentially prevent the brain from establishing more mature neurological pathways for taking in, making sense of, and using information from the world around us. Children with retained reflexes are literally stuck in a pattern of immature and simplistic neurological responses. Many children with neurologically based challenges such as ADHD, autism, learning disabilities, mood disorders, sensory processing disorder, and anxiety have retained reflexes. These reflexes should have integrated early in life, but did not for a variety of reasons. Some of the reasons for retained reflexes include:

- Lack of developmentally appropriate movement opportunities early in life (ex: lack of tummy time as a baby or excessive time spent in walkers/car seats/bouncers)

- Excessive time spent in sedentary activities such as watching television

- Lack of crawling

- Stress during pregnancy and delivery, birth trauma, or complications during and after pregnancy

- Medical illness, physical injuries, traumas, high level of chronic stress

- Exposure to toxins in the environment

When these primitive reflexes persist beyond the time they should, they can interfere with a child's ability to develop more mature motor patterns, sensory integration, eye-hand coordination, memory, learning, and emotional and behavioral regulation. Some signs that a child may have unintegrated primitive reflexes include:

- Feeding difficulties (either as an infant or as an older child)
- Difficulty being soothed by others or self-soothing
- Poor/clumsy motor coordination
- Communication delays
- Thumb sucking past age five
- Difficulties with daytime toilet training past age four
- Chronic bedwetting past age five
- Motion sickness
- Lack of hand dominance
- Hypersensitivity to noise
- Easily over stimulated
- Struggles with learning how to ride a bike or scooter
- Hyperactivity
- Poor attention
- Awkward pencil grasp
- Difficulty with catching or kicking a ball
- Poor ability to copy from the board
- Social difficulties with peers
- Poor impulse control
- Difficulty learning to read and/or comprehend
- Poor handwriting
- Chronic anxiety and fearfulness

- Sleep difficulties
- Chronic negativity and/or low frustration tolerance

If your child is struggling with any of these symptoms or issues, it is helpful to have an evaluation of reflex integration to determine if specific treatment would be beneficial. Such treatment typically includes the use of repetitive movements aimed at integrating the reflex so that the brain can attain a more mature neurological pattern. Depending on the specific treatment approach used, these movements may vary. At our clinic we utilize the Rhythmic Movement Training™ approach, but there are other specific types of reflex integration therapies available as well. Regardless of approach, the prescriptive movements must be done consistently in order for progress to occur.

Even without specific reflex assessment and treatment, there are some key things parents can do to support reflex integration as a whole. Movement is key, and children should be engaged in movement as often as possible throughout the day. The more a child is moving in purposeful ways, the more integrated the brain and body become. Focus on reducing time spent in sedentary activities, and increase the time spent on activities that involve moving the body. This will form a beneficial foundation for reflex integration.

SETH'S STORY

Seth had always been a highly anxious child. He had been diagnosed with autism at age four, but the biggest issue impacting his functioning was his chronically high level of anxiety. His body was constantly tense, as evidenced by chronic toe walking and stiff posture. Seth was resistive to new situations and expectations, and very rigid in his preferences. One of the coping mechanisms he had developed to manage his anxiety was repetitive phrases, and asking questions to which he already knew the answers.

> Reflex assessment showed that Seth had numerous unintegrated primitive reflexes.

It was difficult for him to fully engage in anything going on around him, as he was constantly on high alert for anything that might cause him distress. Anxiety was running his life, as well as that of his parents who were constantly trying to keep things predictable and exactly the way he wanted them in order to reduce his anxiety. While Seth had a number of issues that benefitted from treatment, one of the primary concerns that first needed to be addressed was to reduce his chronic level of anxiety.

Reflex integration was a key component of accomplishing this for him. Reflex assessment showed that Seth had numerous unintegrated primitive reflexes, including the Fear Paralysis Reflex, the Moro Reflex, and the Tonic Labyrinthine Reflex. These were all likely contributing to his tense body posture, toe walking, and chronic anxiety. We began with passive rhythmic movements designed to help integrate these specific reflexes. These passive movements are generally calming for children, and this was the case for Seth.

His parents learned to do the movements, and consistently followed through with them each day for 10-15 minutes. Within a month, Seth's body posture had begun to relax; he was less consumed with asking repetitive questions, and was calmer overall. His mother said, "It seems like his internal spring has started to unwind a little bit."

Over time, and with the progression of integrative movements in treatment, Seth's primitive reflexes began to integrate. He became less anxious, and his body was more relaxed. Within the first six months of movements, he was no longer toe walking throughout the day. Seth's anxiety symptoms also benefitted from other strategies implemented over time including diet changes, nutritional supplements, and parent training. As his anxiety level reduced, he was better able to benefit from everything that was being done at home and school to support his development.

> ▶ **Key Take-Away**
> Unintegrated reflexes can be an underlying factor for many children with attention, anxiety, learning, and behavior challenges. Movement in general, and specific prescriptive movements used in reflex integration therapy, are essential to help children shift from stuck unintegrated patterns of development into more mature patterns of functioning.

Take Movement Breaks

Clearly movement is an essential support to children's learning, focus and overall development. Many children struggle with the requirement to be still for lengthy periods of time, but the reality is that children are required to engage in sedentary activities sometimes. They are also engaging in sedentary activities anytime they are watching television, playing video games, surfing the web, or spending time on their smart phone. Whether the sedentary activity is imposed on them, such as during homework time, or chosen by them, such as playing video games, periodic movement breaks are healthy and appropriate.

Movement breaks support attention and focus during lengthy assignments and tasks. They get the blood flowing and bring more oxygen to the brain, which supports learning and attention. From a visual standpoint, shifting focus from close-up to distance supports healthy vision and visual processing skills. Taking breaks to move also improves mood, and reduces the irritability that can occur with longer periods of sitting. Children struggling with anxiety and perfectionism benefit from putting aside the minor details upon which they are focused to do something completely different and movement oriented.

The frequency and type of movement break varies depending on the age and developmental level of the child. Toddlers have a very brief attention span, often just a few minutes long. Preschoolers can be expected to attend to a sedentary task or lesson for 5-10 minutes at a time before needing a break. Most children in the early grades of elementary school will benefit from movement breaks every 15-20 minutes, depending on the task. Older elementary age children can typically go 20-30 minutes before needing a break. Adolescents and adults should take a break at least once every 45-60 minutes, sometimes sooner depending on the task.

These are general guidelines, and may differ depending on the needs of the child. The point is that no child can or should engage in prolonged sedentary tasks without break periods involving movement. Movement breaks support healthy brain and body function, and help ensure that children are getting the physical activity they need each day.

Some options for brief, simple, and effective movement breaks include:

- Stand and stretch arms and legs

- Walk or march in place

- Walk around the room or house

- Jumping jacks

- Wall push-ups

- Simple yoga poses

- Lunges

- Dance to a song

- Bounce a ball

- Walk to get a drink

- Bounce or roll on an exercise ball

- Pull on Lycra or other stretchy bands

- Jump in place

- Animal walks: jump like a frog, walk like a crab, slither like a snake

- Stand and alternate touching a part on one side of the body with the opposite hand: left foot with right hand, right ear with left hand, etc.

> Movement breaks support attention and focus during lengthy assignments and tasks. They get the blood flowing and bring more oxygen to the brain, which supports learning and attention.

Movement breaks do not have to be long to be effective. Often a 2-3 minute movement break can be beneficial, but even 60 seconds of standing to stretch can help. Most children require parent support and reminders to take breaks during sedentary activities, especially their preferred activities such as video games where children often lose track of time. You may find it helpful to set a timer to help remind you and your children when it's time to get up and move.

Movement breaks can also be used as motivators during non-preferred activities such as homework, as it is helpful for children to know when they will be able to do something different and more stimulating. However you decide to use them, be intentional about allowing and expecting your children to take breaks for movement within and between periods of sedentary activity to best support their development and functioning.

> ► **Key Take-Away**
> Implementing brief movement breaks at appropriate time intervals during sedentary activities supports your child's attention, learning, mood, behavior, vision, and physical health.

Movement Options during School & Homework Time

Do you have a child who reads books while hanging upside down off the edge of the couch? Does your son constantly shake his leg and foot while doing homework? Are you constantly telling your daughter to put her bottom in the chair instead of perching on the chair with her feet or sitting on her knees with her body draped over the table? Some children are constantly seeking out movement, regardless of what they are doing, and it can become frustrating for adults to understand how in the world they can get anything done!

Despite what research says about child development and the importance of movement for learning, the adult tendency is to tell kids to "sit still" when we ask them to work on something.

If you watch how children naturally engage in tasks, you will notice that they move in obvious or subtle ways the majority of the time. Research has shown that movement helps facilitate the learning process,[2] so it makes sense that children naturally seek out ways to stimulate their brains and bodies while learning and engaging in tasks. This is especially the case for children diagnosed with ADHD and related disorders, as these children need more movement in order to learn.[3] Despite what research says about child development and the importance of movement for learning, the adult tendency is to tell kids to "sit still" when we ask them to work on something. This is counterproductive for many children, and may result in poorer focus and performance.

Many adults become concerned that allowing children to move while engaged in school-related or other types of learning tasks will cause disruptions, and reduce children's ability to get their work done. While certain types of chaotic movement certainly can cause disruptions at home and school, the good news is that there are many types of movement activities that can enhance the learning process and be done without disruption. The reality is that children who need movement will find ways to meet that need regardless of what adults desire. It is better to provide children with appropriate movement opportunities to meet those needs in healthy and non-disruptive ways as opposed to forcing children to find their own ways to meet these needs, which may be incompatible with home or classroom expectations.

Here are some ways to provide children with the movement they need while working on assignments at school or homework at home, without causing disruption to others around them. Some of these can also be helpful for situations where children need to sit quietly, such as at a play or church service:

- *Lycra Chair Bands* – Tie a strip of Lycra fabric across the front legs of a chair so your child can fidget and kick against the band. This is a great tool for children who struggle to sit still in a chair, and those who benefit from movement while reading, doing homework, or even eating at the table. Kids can move their feet and legs against the band to experience the organizing pressure and movement, and it doesn't make any noise.

- *Ball Chairs* – Sitting on an exercise ball or ball chair allows children to bounce and move on the ball while working at their desk/table, reading a book, listening to a lesson, etc. One option is to buy a regular exercise ball for your child to sit on. The ball needs to be a size that allows your child's feet to touch the floor. There are ball stands or bases available that help keep the exercise ball in one spot on the floor, as opposed to rolling around. Another option is to purchase a ball chair, which consists of a chair frame with an exercise ball as the seat. There are many types of ball chairs commercially available, including options with wheels, arms, and various types of backs.

- *Fidget Seats* – These are especially helpful for children who like to move around a lot in their chair, as the surface of the seat becomes slightly moveable for them. An inexpensive way to create a fidget seat is to buy a beach ball big enough to cover the seat of the chair, and blow it up slightly. Place the partially inflated ball on the child's seat and have them sit down on it. They should be able to move around on the squishy surface without falling off. There are commercially available fidget seats that can be purchased to essentially do the same thing. Some have textured surfaces that provide additional sensory input. These products go by names such as seating discs, wiggle cushions, and sensory cushions. You may also want to experiment with placing a soft pillow under your child while seated, as it can provide a similar movement experience.

• *T-Stools* – These T-shaped stools require the child to balance in order to stay upright. They allow for movement and wiggling as well. It can take some practice for children to learn how to stay on them, but most children get the hang of it very quickly. These stools not only provide opportunities for movement, but the fact that children have to maintain balance supports their overall focus and attention. There are many varieties of T-stools commercially available, but parents can also make their own if they are handy with those sorts of projects.

• *Rocking Chair* – Some children benefit from a rhythmic rocking movement when learning or engaging with tasks. Rocking chairs are available in a variety of sizes, and the ideal option is one that allows your child's feet to touch the floor.

• *Pace Space* – Use tape on the floor to create a space where your child can walk/pace while reading or listening. Many children do this anyway, but taping off a specific space helps ensure that the child does not leave the area.

• *Ditch the Desk* – Many children with attention, learning, sensory, and behavioral challenges function most poorly when they have to sit on a hard chair at a desk. Allow your child to do homework and other learning tasks in whatever position works best.

Some children may do best lying on their stomach on the floor while propped up on elbows. Others may focus better if they stand at the table or counter to do their work. There are commercially available standing desks that provide a work surface that can be appropriately raised and lowered depending on the height of the person using them. Beanbag chairs, hammocks or other spaces that provide a cocoon-like space are very helpful for some children. Help your child explore seating/space options that best facilitate focus and learning.

• *Treadmills* – Treadmills allow for constant movement without leaving the area. Some children do well reading or completing other assignments while walking on treadmills. There are commercially available treadmill desks that are gaining in popularity due to research showing that adults with sedentary desk jobs are at greater risk for a host of physical and mental health conditions.

MEGAN'S STORY

Megan was in first grade and struggling with the expectation of sitting still in school, and when doing homework. She was often in trouble at school for not sitting still, and had fallen numerous times when tipping and rocking her chair at her desk. At home, her parents were constantly telling her to stop moving while she worked on her homework or ate at the dinner table.

> My starting point was to educate her parents
> about the role of movement in learning.

Megan's parents came to me looking for solutions to their daughter's "hyperactivity" and lack of focus, as school professionals had been hinting to them that they should get Megan diagnosed with ADHD and put on medication. I was quickly able to see that Megan was a very bright little girl. Her parents described her as a joyful child who liked to "dance her way through life." They were not interested in labeling her or giving her medications, but were struggling to figure out how to help her function better in school and when working on homework.

I fully supported the parents in their desire to find strategies to help Megan without unnecessarily diagnosing her or giving her medication to "make her sit still." There were a number of strategies we implemented to support Megan, including some dietary changes, neurofeedback, reflex integration, and parent training. However, my starting point was to educate her parents about the role of movement in learning, and to help them let go of the expectation that she sit still all the time in order to get things done.

We worked together to find ways for Megan to get the movement she needed while still being able to focus on her homework. Parents found that a fidget cushion helped her sit in a chair when needed, while still allowing for some movement. They experimented with different options during homework time, and found that Megan did well when she sat in a large beanbag chair with a lap desk as a work surface. Once they found some workable solutions at home, they spoke with the teacher about options for the classroom.

Some of the options that worked well for her in school were to use her fidget cushion on her desk chair, use a Lycra chair band on the legs of her desk chair, and to lie down in the reading area to read and do worksheets. With these options in place, Megan was able to have the movement stimulation she needed without disturbing others in the classroom.

▶ **Key Take-Away**

Movement enhances learning, and children should be provided options to move in ways that facilitate focus and work completion at home and school.

part five: **connection**

CHAPTER 14

THE POWER
OF CONNECTION

Connection builds and strengthens a
trusting relationship that helps the child
feel secure, cared for, and safe.

H uman beings are wired for connection. We need connection with others in order to grow and thrive. This is especially true of children who require relationships with parents and other trusted adults in order to attain appropriate growth and guidance.[1] The development of cognitive, sensory, motor, communication, emotional, behavioral and relational skills all stem from the connections between children and parents. This is why the quality of the parent-child relationship has such a profound impact on the child's overall development and functioning throughout childhood.

Children require connection with parents and the guidance they provide in order to attain key developmental milestones. As your child ages, connections expand to involve other adults and peers. These relationships become important for the continued growth of communication, cognitive, social and emotional skills. However, the child's ability to connect with others always comes back to the foundational relationship between themselves and their primary caregivers.

> The development of cognitive, sensory, motor, communication, emotional, behavioral and relational skills all stem from the connections between children and parents.

Throughout the chapters in this section, solutions are provided that aim at promoting healthy supportive relational connections between parents and children. When a child has challenges, the parent-child relationship can become disrupted in many ways that lead to unsupportive interactions for both parent and child. All of the parents I have ever worked with have tried their hardest to figure out how to relate and respond to their child in supportive ways that minimize problems.

However, it can be very difficult for parents to know how to manage their child's challenges and symptoms. Often they exhaust their repertoire of ideas and resources, and are left feeling as if nothing can work effectively and consistently. The solutions provided in this chapter will help you feel more competent in managing the challenges that arise with your child, and lead to a stronger relational connection. This, in turn, will help support your child's development in all areas across the board. Parents and children who already have a consistently strong positive relationship will also benefit from these tips and strategies for managing specific difficulties that can arise with children who have attention, anxiety, mood, and behavior difficulties.

Guided Participation

If you think back to when you were a child, chances are many memories of doing things together with a parent or other trusted adult will come to mind. Maybe you helped your mom and dad build a tree house in the backyard. Perhaps you spent time in the kitchen with your grandmother learning to bake. You may have memories of a parent playing catch with you in the backyard as you prepared for Little League season. Maybe you recall sitting with your piano teacher each week as she taught you to play increasingly challenging songs. Regardless of the specific memories, you can recall meaningful times spent with key adults as they guided you to develop new skills and abilities. You were a little apprentice engaged with the masters as they facilitated your learning and discovery about the world.

This process is called *guided participation*, and it is fundamental for helping children learn, grow, and develop into capable and independent individuals.

Guided participation refers to the process where children gain new skills and knowledge through active participation alongside parents and other experienced adults. The term was first developed by psychologist, Lev Vygotsky. He identified that this guiding relationship between parents/adults and children is necessary for appropriate child development across many domains.[2] When guided participation is not firmly in place, the child cannot learn the vast number of skills and concepts required to move toward independent function.

Adults understand how the world works, and are already proficient in the cognitive, social, motor, and communication skills needed to navigate and function in the world. Children are born with none of these skills or knowledge, but learn from the modeling and guidance of the adults around them. When this guided participation gets disrupted, children lack the opportunities necessary to move forward toward greater independent functioning.

Guided participation is about showing, teaching and guiding your child to learn new things, not just doing things for him. When disrupted, your child misses opportunities that allow for greater independent functioning.

There are many ways the guided participation relationship can be disrupted from both the parent and child perspectives. Children's symptoms, including inattention, anxiety, irritability, hyperactivity, processing problems and dysregulated behaviors can get in the way of the guided participation relationship. These challenges may lead the child to resist participating in activities with parents; or the child may desire participation, but struggles to stick with the process and learn from it. It can be very frustrating and discouraging for parents who try to engage children in activities only to have the child disrupt the process in various ways.

On the parent end of things, the guided participation relationship can become disrupted when the parent feels highly anxious and/ or avoids including the child in activities because they tend not to go well. It is understandable that adults would avoid, either consciously or unconsciously, including their child in activities if the child is consistently very dysregulated, anxious, irritable or resistive. Many times, parents feel it is easier to just take care of things themselves. While this is understandable, it has a negative impact on the child's overall development.

Guided participation is about showing, teaching and guiding your children to learn new things, not just doing things for them. One of the most important things you can do to support child development is to include your child in as many guided participation activities throughout the day as possible. If your child is highly resistive to being guided with anything, start on very simple tasks for brief moments. For example, your child may resist unloading the dishwasher with you, and you may dread 15 minutes of fighting, arguing and cajoling to get it done.

A more appropriate starting point may be to have your child help you put a couple of items away, and then allow the child to leave the activity. Once the child can calmly and competently put away a couple of items, you can begin to increase the responsibilities and the length of participation. Start small, if needed, and work up from there.

Identify ways to give your child a role in as many activities of daily living as possible. Even young or very impaired children can take simple roles in activities such as throwing clothing in the hamper, putting dirty dishes in the sink, feeding the dog, shredding junk mail, and throwing away their own trash. Set the expectation that your child will participate in these tasks, and provide guidance to see the process through as needed. Chores and activities of daily living are excellent options, as they are things parents need to spend time on anyway. Consider tasks such as doing dishes, sorting laundry, getting the mail, wiping the counters, putting away the groceries, and everything else you do around your home on a regular basis. These are all ways to engage your child in guided participation.

You will also want to look for opportunities for your child to watch you perform tasks he is not yet ready to complete on his own. When you do the laundry, for example, have your child there with you. Find a simple role, such as helping put dirty clothes in the washer, and then complete the rest while he observes. Including your child as an observer is a valuable way to improve cognition and skills for everyday life activities. It is never too early to start including your child in these tasks, and it's also never too late. Start setting the expectation that your child will participate, at least as an observer.

There are some key elements that increase the likelihood that you and your child will have a successful experience in a guided participation activity, including the following:

- *Provide a role for your child that is within his competence level.* When you expect too much, the child will end up feeling frustrated and incompetent. Giving a role that is too easy does not challenge your child, and will not promote growth.

- *Do not leave your child alone to do his role in isolation.* Remember that the goal is to learn from your guidance and modeling. Look at ways you can work together to accomplish tasks. This supports a healthy relationship and developmental growth at the same time!

- *Support your child as needed.* When your child encounters a challenge, avoid the impulse to jump in and do the task yourself. Likewise, do not allow your child to continually struggle on his own for too long. You can provide support by demonstrating, guiding hand-over-hand, or starting the process and allowing him to finish. You want to provide enough support that the child can successfully complete his role, but not so much that the child feels you did it without his help.

- *Encourage your child by spotlighting the role he did, and what you accomplished together.* Simply saying "good job" is not ideal, as it doesn't help the child internalize what was done well. Be specific in your praise by saying things like: "We got all those dishes put away!" "You did an awesome job getting the mail out of the box." Or, "I appreciate how carefully you placed the folded clothes in the drawer."

- *As your child masters one role, be conscious of increasing the challenge and complexity.* If your child has mastered putting away the clean silverware, consider next steps such as putting away the cups or plates. A child who is independently able to sort his own laundry may be ready for a next step of putting the load in the washer, and starting it or measuring laundry soap to put in the machine. Look for opportunities to increase your child's skills and sense of competence in as many tasks throughout the day as possible.

- *Find something to do together with your child each day.* The task or activity doesn't have to be huge, as even little moments working on something together make a difference. Simple tasks and brief moments can create powerful opportunities for creating positive memories, building a sense of competence, and strengthening the relationship.

OLIVER'S STORY

At 18 years old, Oliver had just completed high school and was sitting in his parents' home playing video games all day. He had been diagnosed over the years with Asperger's Disorder, anxiety, oppositional defiance disorder, depression, and learning disabilities. Oliver managed to get through high school, but it is questionable whether he or his special education teachers and paraprofessionals did more of the work to get him his diploma. His parents had always done everything for him, as evidenced by the fact that Oliver had never had expectations to do chores, prepare his own food, clean up after himself, or do anything at home that required effort. Now faced with the rest of his life beyond high school, Oliver had no skills or motivation; his parents had no idea what to do with him.

His parents explained that anytime they ever tried to have him do anything with them, he refused—even from a very young age. Eventually they gave up, as it was exhausting and upsetting to them. As they reflected back on the past 18 years, they realized that at some point they just gave up trying to guide Oliver with anything. They made sure he got to school each day, but beyond that, they allowed him to do what he wanted as long as he was not causing a problem for anyone. One year led to the next, and here they were with an 18-year-old son who did not have any skills for independently managing himself in daily tasks and activities, and even worse, with no sense that he needed to do them.

Both parents were determined that he would not end up having other people take care of him for the rest of his life while he sat playing video games, but they were not sure how to start setting new expectations and teaching him how to do the real world things he needed to do. One of the first things I worked on was helping Oliver's parents understand that there were actions they could take now, even at age 18, to help him become more capable and independent.

I helped them identify that one reason Oliver was so anxious, depressed, and unmotivated was that he lacked a sense of personal competence. Just as they had given up long ago trying to include him in anything, Oliver had given up trying because he decided he was going to be unsuccessful no matter what he did. We needed to identify some simple starting points for parents to guide Oliver with basic tasks throughout the day. I had his parents start with very basic things such as handing him a grocery bag to carry in when they exited the car after shopping. They also set the expectation that Oliver would help clear the table after meals, and would work with his mother to sort his laundry each week.

Not surprisingly, Oliver initially resisted some of these responsibilities; so I helped his parents develop appropriate motivators, such as tying his electronics access to completion of these brief simple tasks. Once he was competently completing these simple tasks, we began to increase the expectations and challenges. It was slow going initially, as anything Oliver perceived as "too hard" or "unfair" would send him into a mode of resistance and avoidance. His parents kept at it and I continued to support them in riding out the challenges he presented to the process.

Over the course of a year, Oliver began doing his laundry with very little assistance, making his own snacks, helping prepare family meals when requested, doing indoor and outdoor chores with his parents, along with other tasks and responsibilities. Beyond the improvement in his skill level, the most marked improvement in Oliver was his sense of personal competence. He began to see himself as a person who could do things, a person who could tackle challenges, and a person who could learn new skills without falling apart. His parents' efforts with guided participation were rewarded with a son who began to engage and function in ways that would lead him toward greater independence.

▶ **Key Take-Away**

The guided participation relationship between parents and children is essential for supporting child development across all domains in order for children to attain the highest degree of competence and independence possible.

CHAPTER 15

STAY CALM

Staying calm when children are not is a critical strategy
for effectively managing challenging behaviors.

D o you have trouble staying calm when your child is distressed
or throws a temper tantrum? Do you lose your cool when your
child becomes defiant or has a meltdown? If so, you are not alone.
Many parents find it difficult to stay calm and in control when their
child is upset and dysregulated. While it may be hard, staying calm
when children are not is a critical strategy for effectively managing
challenging behaviors. In fact, this ability forms a crucial foundation
for all other strategies parents may implement for their child.

Below are five reasons staying calm is such an important
component of connecting with children:

- *A child's ability to stay calm, or return to a calm state, is depen-*
  dent on the adult's ability to remain calm. Children mirror
  the emotions of trusted adults, and will calm or escalate

in response to the parent's emotions. When the adult gets upset, the child escalates even more. Parents who remain calm in their voice and actions will help the child return to a calm state more quickly.

- *Staying calm provides the child with a helpful model.* Many children with developmental and mental health concerns do not realize that it is possible to stay calm when they feel distressed. When parents stay calm, it allows the child to see that it is possible to avoid escalating in the face of a difficult situation. It also allows the child to match his voice and actions to how the adult is responding.

- *Not inserting parent emotions into the mix allows the child to more quickly process the situation and return to a calmer baseline.* Children with challenging behaviors are often upset and dysregulated because they are overwhelmed and not processing information well. Inserting strong adult emotions into the mix only causes more confusion and overwhelms the child, requiring more time for the child to process and return to a calm baseline.

- *When parents stay calm, it helps keep them from saying or doing things they will later regret.* Our first inclination of what to say or do often involves things that we may regret after the intensity of the situation is over. By staying calm and composed, you can refrain from comments and actions that exacerbate the situation and make you feel badly afterward.

- *Finally, staying calm in the heat of the moment allows you to build and maintain a relationship of trust and safety with your children.* They need to know that you have their backs, and will be able to stay composed and in control—regardless of how out of control they become.

This builds and strengthens a trusting relationship that helps the child feel secure, cared for, and safe. I would argue that nothing is more important than this for helping a child with attention, anxiety, mood, and behavior challenges improve behavior and functioning in general.

Most parents may have a desire to remain calm with their children, but struggle to know how to do it. It is easy to get swept up in the emotions of stressful moments, and many adults struggle to manage their own feelings when their child is upset. Before providing specific strategies for staying calm, I think it is helpful to explain the basics of what is going on in the brain of a person who is experiencing intense emotions such as anxiety or anger.

> It is essential that parents remain as calm and controlled as possible when a child is getting emotionally agitated.

As the emotions build, the child's brain goes into a "fight-flight-freeze" mode. Their brain assesses that the situation is creating upset, and it sends a message to the body to get ready to fight or flee. The body then gets physiologically ready for one of those responses: breathing gets more shallow, muscles tense, heart rate increases, and the body readies to face what it perceives is a major threat.

These physiological responses send signals to the brain that there is in fact something to be very upset about. This ongoing cycle causes the brain to shut down all processes it deems as not essential at that moment. One of the first parts of the brain to shut down is the pre-frontal cortex which is responsible for higher-level rational thinking. When this happens, we are not capable of processing higher-level language or logically processing information in general. This is why we have all had the experience of saying and doing things we don't mean "in the heat of the moment."

It is not until our body starts to calm and the brain perceives that the threat has passed, that our pre-frontal cortex comes back online. You are then capable of rational thinking. It is essential that parents remain as calm and controlled as possible when a child is getting emotionally agitated. Our goal needs to be to help them perceive that the threat has passed so that their body and brain can return more quickly to a calm and rational baseline.

With all this in mind, here are some dos and don'ts to help you help your child come out of a state of anxiety or upset more quickly:

- *Do stay as quiet as possible.* Bring your volume down in response to the child's rising volume.

- *Don't yell or raise your voice* in an effort to be heard by the child.

Staying quiet helps prevent overwhelm, and allows your child to see that you are a calm and safe presence in that moment. When you raise your voice, you risk your child perceiving you as an increasing threat, which perpetuates their fight-flight-freeze response.

- *Do make calm simple statements* acknowledging that the child is upset.

- *Don't make demands* or ask questions.

Using a lot of language during moments of overwhelm and upset only compounds a child's processing difficulties. Keeping your language simple and supportive reduces the perception of threat, and helps restore calm more quickly. Remember that in these moments your child is not capable of processing and responding to higher level language, so asking questions and making demands is likely to increase their frustration and upset.

- *Do stay physically close* to provide a boundary.

- *Don't try to move the child* or otherwise physically manage the child unless there is a safety issue.

Staying physically close to your child, even holding a hand if needed, helps prevent running away or unsafe physical behavior. It is important that these situations do not turn into a free-for-all where parents are chasing children while they go wherever they want. On the other hand, you do not want to physically force or drag your child. Such physical management is perceived as threatening and will continue the escalation. Ensure that your child is in a safe place where physical harm cannot occur. Stay physically close to ensure that your child doesn't run away. Then calmly stand or sit by your child until the distress has passed.

- *Do keep your focus* on allowing your child to return to a calm baseline.

- *Don't try to rationalize,* make a point, or teach a lesson. Don't try to negotiate.

If a parent is focused on getting their child to recognize what he has done wrong, asking their child to make a different choice or negotiating with their child to stop the behavior, then the child will likely continue to perceive the situation as threatening. During these episodes, the focus needs to be on providing support for the child to return to a rational brain state. Trying to teach a lesson or negotiate for better behavior will generally backfire by fueling the escalation.

- *Do quietly and calmly* tell/lead your child to whatever is happening next once he is calm.

- *Don't try to discuss the situation* immediately after your child calms down, attempt to make your child apologize, or try to get your child to agree that he acted inappropriately.

Once your child is calm, it is important simply to move on to whatever is next. If the parent attempts to discuss the situation immediately, impose a punishment or get an apology, there is a high risk of sending the child right back into a dysregulated state. If there is discussion that needs to occur, it is best to do it well after the fact when the child has been in a calm state for a good period of time.

Don't pour salt in the wound by embarrassing your child, or instilling guilt or shame about the behavior. Allow your child the dignity to successfully move on to whatever needs to happen next, which may include calmly helping to clean things up or put things back in order if there was any disarray in the environment.

- *Do keep your mind in the present moment.*

- *Don't let your mind go far into the future* to think about what your child's behavior will be like, and how you will manage it.

When parents allow their mind to focus on the negative in a situation, especially as this relates to never ending problems in the future, it becomes very difficult to remain calm. Staying calm is much easier for parents when we focus on the here-and-now, and not allow ourselves to conceive the entire day, week, year, or lifetime of the relationship into a never ending catastrophe just because the child is upset in that moment. Staying focused on the goal of being a calm supportive presence in the now will help the situation resolve more quickly.

- *Do keep your breathing slow, steady and deep;* keep your muscles relaxed in order to help your brain stay in a calm and focused state.

- *Don't allow your body to cause increased upset and anxiety* by taking quick shallow breaths, or tensing up.

The mind tends to follow the body, which means that keeping the body calm helps keep the mind calm. Instead of letting your mind spin with upset, try focusing on your breathing. There are many different ways to breathe in order to promote calm and relaxation. A simple technique is to focus on breathing in for a slow count of three, and then breathing out for a slow count of three. It doesn't so much matter how you do it, because just focusing on breathing at a more slow and steady rate will help you maintain calm.

The same goes for muscle tension. Be aware of muscle tenseness, and aim to keep your muscles as relaxed as possible. This includes being especially aware of tension in your facial muscles, as a tense face can make adults look more threatening to the child!

Any parent who has been faced with a dysregulated child can attest that staying calm is rarely an instinctual response. It can take practice for parents to stay calm when their child is escalating and upset. Hopefully you now have some ideas to support this process, and some practical tips to use the next time you face a challenging emotional situation with your child. While it may take practice, learning to stay calm when your child is upset is well worth the effort.

> **Key Take-Away**
>
> A parent's ability to stay calm when their child is distressed or angry is critical for managing the situation in a way that promotes calming, and builds a positive relationship between parent and child.

CHAPTER 16

COMMUNICATION STRATEGIES

When a child's brain is not able to process
verbal information quickly and logically,
one of the least effective things parents
can do is talk a lot.

Many children with attention, anxiety, mood, and behavior challenges have difficulty taking in and making sense of information from the environment quickly and effectively— particularly language. Those who have appropriate language processing skills under typical circumstances tend to experience a breakdown in those skills during times of stress, fear or upset. When language processing breaks down, the child has more difficulty making sense of what is said and responding appropriately. All parents have experienced this at one point or another, often when in the midst of a very stressful, overwhelming or frightening situation.

When a child's brain is not able to process verbal information quickly and logically, whether that is because of a disability or the specific situation, one of the least effective things parents can do is talk a lot. Parents tend to use a high amount of verbal communication with children—especially when there is a problem, or they are trying to teach a lesson or make a point. This can be very problematic for children who have processing deficits or are simply too stressed, overwhelmed or upset to make sense of things in the moment.

Using less verbal communication when children are experiencing breakdowns in language processing is a key strategy to support the child's ability to regain calm, make sense of what is happening, and respond more appropriately.

Saying less is helpful for many reasons:

- *Using fewer words reduces the language processing demands, and allows your child to more effectively think about what has been said.* Children with processing difficulties, which includes many children with attention, anxiety, mood, and behavior challenges, often struggle to quickly make sense of what is being said. The more that is said to them the further behind they get in terms of trying to make sense of things. Reducing the amount of verbal communication helps them process more efficiently and effectively, and dramatically reduce the stress level involved.

- *Using fewer words during difficult periods helps reduce the emotions in the moment, which allows the child to calm more quickly.* Parents often use emotionally charged verbal communication to make a point or teach a lesson. This tends to be an ineffective strategy, as the child's brain is not in a rational processing mode that allows for understanding what is being said. Attempting to talk to your child during these moments generally serves to exacerbate frustration and upset. Wait to talk through the situation after the fact, when your child is calm.

• *Remaining quiet is an effective strategy to use in situations when your child is distressed or angry and is being argumentative, verbally aggressive, or attempting to negotiate.* Staying quiet in these moments models calm, thoughtful interaction during heated situations. It also reduces the amount of information your child has to process, which helps the calming process. Using less verbal communication also shows your child that you are not going to engage with any hostile or inappropriate communication or behavior. Stay calm and quiet. When your child has ceased the verbal barrage, you can calmly engage in appropriate discussion about the situation.

• *If you have a child who becomes verbally perseverative, stating the same things over and over, speaking less is an effective strategy for reducing this behavior.* These children get stuck on a specific thought, request, word, etc., and struggle to move past it. Some children repeat lines from movies; others may ask the same questions repeatedly or pester constantly with talking about the same topics or issues. This can quickly become exhausting and irritating to parents and everyone else around the child!

When the parent responds to all of this verbalization on the part of the child, it generally perpetuates the behavior. A more effective approach is to verbally disengage with the child when he is talking about repetitive things. It is appropriate to let the child know that you are not going to talk with him about whatever it is he is verbalizing, and then follow through by staying quiet. Some parents have found that putting on a pair of headphones or ear buds provides a helpful visual cue that they will not be engaging with the child in those repetitive loops of verbal perseveration.

Using minimal verbal communication with children during these situations help them better understand the effect this behavior has on others, and sends a clear message that you will not engage in these repetitive go-nowhere exchanges.

- *When you talk less, your nonverbal communication is spotlighted.* Nonverbal communication includes gestures, facial expressions, emotional tone, and physical proximity. Understanding and using nonverbal communication is a deficit for many children with neurodevelopmental disorders.[1] These children may struggle to connect the nonverbal and verbal aspects of communication, which can lead to misreading nonverbal cues from others and poorer understanding and use of communication across the board.

  One of the most effective ways to strengthen a child's ability to understand and use nonverbal communication is by spotlighting your own nonverbal communication. Often when there is a lot of verbal communication going on, your child is focused on that instead of the nonverbal elements of the interaction. By reducing or removing words, your child is forced to be more aware of the nonverbal communication you are using. This can be especially helpful during times when a child is very frustrated, upset, fearful, or angry.

Reducing parent verbal communication during these times allows the child to focus on the calm emotional tone, close comforting physical proximity, supportive facial expressions and gestures from the parent.

> When in doubt, parents would be wise to speak less in order to communicate more effectively.

- *A common issue parents face with children is getting them to listen the first time something is said.* I call this "lazy listening." It occurs when children develop the habit of not processing and responding to communication the first time because they know it will be said again. Parents often lament that their children do not seem to pay attention to what is being said, which leads to them sounding like a broken record as they repeat themselves over and over again. When parents constantly repeat their requests, questions and statements, it can have the effect of teaching children to tune out the majority of what they say; or at least, it teaches them that they do not need to listen the first time something is said.

Instead, parents should focus on saying something once, and expect the child to listen and respond. Constantly repeating yourselves just leads to frustration and fatigue for you, and does little to help children develop the skills for listening and responding to communication. Saying less can mean saying something one time and refusing to repeat it, even if that means the child may experience some unfortunate consequences.

Excessive talking can negatively impact a child's ability to make sense of a situation, may exacerbate upset, leads to "lazy listening" and can increase stress. Relationship breakdowns with parents can also result. Reducing the amount of verbal communication can help children make sense of the situation, return to calm more quickly, listen and respond the first time, all while preserving a supportive relationship. Some children may benefit from less talking throughout the day, while others may need this approach only during challenging moments. When in doubt, parents would be wise to speak less in order to communicate more effectively.

COLIN'S STORY

Colin, age nine and diagnosed with autism, anxiety, and language disorder, easily got stuck in repetitive patterns of verbal behavior. He would repeat lines from Disney movies, specific questions to which he already knew the answer, or things someone had said to him previously. This generally happened when he was feeling anxious, frustrated, or wanted something he was told he couldn't have. His parents were frustrated and tired from constantly listening and responding to Colin's verbal perseveration.

I worked with them to understand the root of this behavior, which was Colin's processing difficulties and subsequent strong uncomfortable emotions. Initially, I explained that reducing verbal communication with Colin would help reduce the anxiety and overwhelm he experienced due to his difficulties with language processing His parents were hesitant to try this strategy, as they had spent many years and a significant amount of money on therapy to get Colin to talk. They were concerned that reducing their verbal communication with him was going to lead to less talking on his end. I assured them that his ability to talk would not be harmed by this approach, and that his communication overall would actually get stronger as a result.

We started with focusing on saying things slowly, and not repeating themselves constantly. They focused on using nonverbal gestures and communication with Colin rather than talking at him all the time. When he would get stuck in one of his perseverative verbal episodes, they would stay quiet and not verbally engage with him. After just a few weeks, his parents noted Colin was more attentive to them; was responding more appropriately to their verbal communication; and that his episodes of verbal perseveration were becoming shorter. They were feeling less stressed and worn out, because they weren't constantly engaging in his stuck verbal cycles. Colin's chronically high level of anxiety seemed to be reducing as well.

Over time, and with continued implementation of this and other strategies, Colin's communication, anxiety, and behavior continued to improve. His parents continue to monitor the amount of verbal communication they use with him, particularly during more complex or emotionally charged situations, to ensure that they are not overwhelming his processing abilities and causing increased frustration or upset.

▶ **Key Take-Away**

Reducing verbal communication, especially during moments when the child is stuck, frustrated, upset, or anxious, helps the child more effectively process language, reduces stress, and promotes a supportive relationship between parent and child.

Use Statements More Than Questions

The style and tone of communication parents use with children can either support or detract from the relationship between them.

While typical human communication involves a much higher proportion of statements and comments than questions, adult communication with children with challenges can be heavily dominated by direct questions. Whereas statements and comments convey more supportive open-ended communication, direct questions tend to lead to parent-dominated interaction that shuts down the communication process.

It can be easy to fall into a mode of constantly asking direct questions of children, especially when you feel it's the only way to get an answer out of them. However, direct questioning can have the effect of shutting down communication and promoting thoughtless exchanges that do not promote meaningful engagement. Anyone who's asked a child, "What did you do in school today?" is all too familiar with the counterproductive effect a direct question can have.

This type of question generally leads to a one or two word response, and does not promote conversation or thoughtful processing of communication. "Nothing," is the typical response! For children with significant communication and language deficits, it is especially crucial to model variety in communication; and this requires branching out beyond closed questions and responses.

It can be easy to fall into a mode of constantly asking direct questions of children, especially when you feel it's the only way to get an answer out of them.

There are numerous reasons why using direct questions as a primary communication style with children can be problematic. Primarily, statements or comments are more supportive of communication and relationship development. Consider the following:

- *Being on the receiving end of questioning can feel uncomfortable and demanding.* When adults are constantly asking questions of a child, it can feel to the child like he is under intense pressure to respond. No one likes to feel barraged with questions all day long! Statements feel less demanding, take the pressure off, and set a tone for more supportive communication between parent and child.

- *Direct questions, particularly closed questions that imply a specific response, do not encourage children to think about what was said and generate unique responses.* Consider the difference between asking a child, "Did you do your homework?" and saying, "I'm not sure if your homework is done yet." The question requires just a yes/no response, and does not promote thinking on the part of the child. The statement, on the other hand, requires the child to actively think through what was said in order to generate his own response. This helps the child develop higher-level thinking and communication skills.

- *Constant direct questioning does not model typical human communication.* While the majority of the communication you use involves statements and comments, it is often the case that adults use a high proportion of direct questions with children who have developmental challenges. Sometimes parents do this because they are concerned they will not get a response from the child if they do not ask a direct question that requires a specific response. However, all children benefit from adults modeling typical communication, regardless of their level of development. Exposing them to comments and statements provides a more appropriate model of communication than relying almost exclusively on questions.

- *Asking children pointed questions can lead to increased impulsive lying behavior because they feel forced to respond in a way that avoids getting into trouble.* Consider the example of a parent who knows that his child ate the last cookie without permission. Asking, "Did you eat the last cookie?" is almost guaranteeing that the child will impulsively say "No," even if he did eat the cookie. The parent has now backed the child into a corner, and lying is the strategy many children use to get out of an uncomfortable situation.

  Making a statement in this situation would be a more effective way to address it. Statements along the lines of "I see you ate the last cookie" or "There are no more cookies" do not allow the child to impulsively respond with a "yes" or "no" answer. Instead, these statements require some thought before responding. While some children may still lie in an effort to avoid getting into trouble, the tone of the interaction between parent and child is more supportive; and it portrays less of a "you've been caught doing something bad" intent.

- *Direct questions tend to convey an expectation of immediate response on the part of the child.* This can lead to children responding without thinking, with some children giving responses that aren't connected to the question that was asked. This can especially be the case in children diagnosed with autism, ADHD, anxiety, auditory processing deficits, or language processing problems. These children are often in such a rush to say something in response to questions that they blurt out whatever comes to mind first, often without thinking about what was actually asked. Using statements is a simple solution to this problem, as statements do not imply the need to rush to response. They encourage more thoughtful processing and responses on the part of the child.

- *Some children develop a habit of responding with "I don't know" whenever they are asked a direct question.* Generally, "I don't know" means they don't want to think about it, don't want to talk about it, or aren't even paying any attention to what is being said. Statements combat this problem by not lending themselves to an "I don't know" response.

> Asking children pointed questions can lead to increased impulsive lying behavior because they feel forced to respond in a way that avoids getting into trouble.

The first step in shifting communication style is becoming aware of how often you use direct questions with your child, as opposed to statements or comments. You may be surprised to discover how often you ask direct questions, or you may find that you use a good balance of questions and comments. If you find that your communication is very question oriented, begin focusing on shifting from questions to statements. Consider how you can turn the questions you would typically ask into statement or comment form, as in the following examples:

- *"Did you hang up your backpack?"* can become " In five minutes I'm going to check to make sure your backpack is on the hook."
- *"What did you do at school today?"* can shift to "I bet you made something cool in art class."

- *"How many times do I have to tell you to get in the shower?"* may be more effectively stated as "I'm frustrated that I've reminded you to get in the shower, and you're still sitting in the living room."

- *"What's the matter?"* may elicit a richer response when phrased as "It looks like something is bothering you."

Your child may not respond to your statements or comments right away, and that is nothing to worry about. Some children may need more time to process what is being said in order to generate a response. In this case, it is important to leave "think time" for the child after making your statement. Don't immediately ask a question or respond for them if they don't respond right away. Give time for them to process and respond in some way.

Other children may ignore your comment in the hope that you will leave them alone or try again with a direct question that doesn't require thought on their part. Again, allow processing time and wait expectantly for a response. Regardless of the reasons why children may respond more slowly or try to avoid responding, continue to work at it so your children get accustomed to engaging in richer and more effective communication.

Begin bringing your awareness to the current state of your communication with your child, and look for ways to incorporate more statements and comments. If you catch yourself asking lots of questions, simply rephrase and try again in a statement form. It can take time to shift your communication style, but the time and effort spent is well worth the result of helping children become more engaged and thoughtful in their own communication.

► **Key Take-Away**

Statements set a supportive tone for communication between parent and child, reduce impulsive responses, and encourage development of thoughtful communication and language processing skills.

CHAPTER 17

SLOW DOWN
AND SIMPLIFY

Children with learning, mood, and behavior
challenges generally function better when activities
and communication operate at a pace they can manage.

The pace of life can get hectic, and children with attention, anxiety, mood, and behavior challenges often do not function at their best in fast-paced situations. Remember, these children have brains that can struggle to take in, make sense of, and respond to information and input from the environment. As a result, the faster the pace of activities and communication the more stress and processing breakdowns can occur. It is important to slow down the pace of communication, actions, activities, and life in general to allow them to catch up with what is happening around them.

Hectic schedules can exacerbate attention, anxiety, mood, and behavior challenges in children. Beyond that, over scheduling tends to make everyone in the family more irritable, overwhelmed, and stressed out!

Here are some key areas to consider for slowing down with children:

- *Pace of daily schedule*–An increasing problem for many families is that of over scheduling. This can happen when children and parents are involved in many activities that consistently create a fast-paced tight schedule. While some activities are beneficial for children, it is generally not good for them to have every moment of their days planned. I have worked with children who are enrolled in so many extracurricular activities and therapies—in addition to full days at school—that they scarcely have time to do anything of their own choosing.

  Hectic schedules can exacerbate attention, anxiety, mood, and behavior challenges in children. Beyond that, over scheduling tends to make everyone in the family more irritable, overwhelmed, and stressed out! Parents and children need to have a relationship that goes beyond constantly moving from one scheduled activity to the next, with parents in the primary role of taxi driver for the child. Consider the overall pace of your child and family's schedule to determine if slowing down the general pace of life would be beneficial for your child and family.

- *Pace of activities*–Children with attention, anxiety, mood, and behavior challenges benefit more from engaging in activities with a slower pace. This goes for activities ranging from cooking together, to getting ready for bed, to playing games. The more rushed the pacing, the more challenging it is for children to focus on what is happening, the more stress and anxiety is provoked, and the less thoughtful engagement can occur. Allow more time than you think may be necessary to avoid rushing your child.

During activities, leave time for your child to think and respond to questions, comments and directions. Don't jump in right away to hurry them along. Leave time for your child to process what was said or done, and to respond.

- *Downtime during the day*–Everyone needs downtime throughout the day, and you become grumpy and stressed if you don't get it! Periods of down time, whether they involve sitting and doing nothing, having a snack, taking a walk, or doing a preferred relaxing activity, allow you to recharge your batteries in order to face whatever tasks and challenges the rest of the day requires. Children need more periods of downtime, especially if they are younger or have more significant challenges. It often works best to alternate periods of activity, or greater challenges and task demands, with periods of down-time. This allows the child to rest and recover in order to tackle the next requirement or challenge.

  Children who struggle to keep their brains focused, are chronically anxious, have depressed or irritable moods, or who have behavior regulation difficulties become tired much more quickly than the typical child. Providing ample opportunities for downtime throughout the day allows them to get the rest and relaxation they need.

  It is important to note here that downtime does not equate to time spent on electronic devices. While children may prefer these activities and believe they are calming and relaxing, the reality is that these activities are highly stimulating from a brain perspective. Some downtime may be appropriately spent watching television or playing a game on the tablet, but downtime needs to consist of other relaxing and less stimulating options as well.

- *Wait time*–When children process information more slowly, it is common for adults to jump in and do things for them, verbally respond for them, or continue making demands or asking the same questions. Allow time for processing after asking questions, giving instructions, or making statements is critical to helping children listen, process, and respond on their own. The amount of wait time required varies from one child to the next and depends on the child's age, developmental level, symptom severity, and specific situation. Some children benefit from just an extra second or two of wait time to respond, while others may need a minute or longer.

  Experiment with waiting longer than you typically would to see how long it takes for your child to verbally respond or take action. You may be surprised at the difference a few extra seconds can make, and how it reduces the amount of verbal repetition and prompting you are doing as a parent.

Children with learning, mood, and behavior challenges generally function better when activities and communication operate at a pace they can manage. Avoiding over scheduling, leaving some extra time within and between activities, allowing for processing time after asking questions or giving instructions, and providing appropriate amounts of downtime throughout the day can go a long way to reducing anxiety, improving mood, and enhancing overall function for children and their parents.

> ▶ **Key Take-Away**
> Slowing down the pace of activities and communication can have a positive impact on a child's ability to process information, stay calm and relaxed, and respond to task demands throughout the day. It also leads to a more positive supportive relationship between parent and child.

Simplify

Children with attention, anxiety, mood, and behavior challenges can be easily overwhelmed, discouraged, and resistive even to things you feel are appropriate and reasonable for them. Every parent has encountered situations with their child where the task, activity or expectation was just too complex—and the entire thing ended badly!

Perhaps you took your child grocery shopping on a Saturday morning and the store was crowded. Fifteen minutes into the experience, your child was having a meltdown. Maybe you tried to have a happy family game night; except midway through the game your child started losing focus, grabbed everyone's game pieces, and then refused to finish the game. You may even have a child who balks at or resists situations or activities beyond a small range of familiar and preferred options.

> We need to remember that "perception is reality;" and this means that if a child perceives something is too difficult, anxiety provoking or overwhelming, then it is.

Situations that are overly complex can be frustrating and create a sense of incompetence for children and parents. It is important to note that children and adults often have differing perceptions of what is reasonable and manageable. Remember that "perception is reality." This means that if a child perceives something is too difficult, anxiety provoking or overwhelming, then it is. Regardless of what the adult thinks, the child has to work up to seeing that the situation can be managed successfully and comfortably.

When tasks or situations feel too complicated to a child, the tendency is to avoid or resist participation. This is a natural response to fearing overwhelm or failure. It is important, therefore, to simplify activities and situations so the child feels competent and successful. Children need to have a meaningful role in any activity, but that role or expectation needs to be something they can manage without overwhelm. The key is to start with something simple, and add complexity as the child can manage it.

There are many ways to simplify activities, including the following:

- *The more people that are involved, the more complex the activity or situation will be.* Include only the number of people that is manageable for your child. A birthday party may be more successful and comfortable for your child if there are only four or five other children in attendance, rather than ten. Playing a game with your child may be more workable if the child plays with the parents only, rather than all the siblings. Consider how overwhelmed and anxious your child becomes in the situation, and then adjust the number of people involved accordingly.

- *The environment can make a big difference in the success of an activity.* Children who become easily overwhelmed or have difficulty focusing attention will likely do better in environments with less stimulation. The more challenges the child has, the simpler the environment should be in order to support successful participation. Reduce environmental distractors: turn the TV or radio off; select a room without lots of visual distractions; and make sure your child is positioned in an area where they don't have the ability to easily leave the activity or fiddle with items not involved in the task.

- *Consider the role that is most appropriate for your child to take.* Any task or activity can be divided up into specific jobs or roles for each person. Matching the demands of the role to the needs of the child is key to ensuring success. Making cookies, for example, can have many different roles such as gathering ingredients, measuring, mixing, placing dough on baking sheets and putting them in the oven.

Depending on the age and abilities of the child, certain roles may be more or less appropriate. A younger or more impaired child may be successful with mixing the batter, or helping the parent pour premeasured ingredients into the bowl. An older or more developmentally mature child may be able to handle the role of measuring ingredients, or placing cookies on the baking sheet.

Being intentional about roles and responsibilities is helpful when expecting your child to tackle a larger project such as cleaning the bedroom. This kind of activity is comprised of many different roles and tasks, and expecting a child to tackle the entire process alone may lead to a breakdown. Instead, break the activity into smaller pieces and assign specific roles. You may even help your child with it, and divide the roles between the two of you. It may also be appropriate to give your child one role at a time such as picking up the Legos, putting dirty clothing in the hamper, or gathering trash to put in the garbage. In the context of an activity like homework, you may divide up roles and have your child generate responses while you write them down.

There are endless ways to divide up roles and responsibilities within tasks and activities, and the goal is to match the complexity of the role to the ability level and frustration tolerance of your child.

- *Adjusting the timing is another way to simplify activities for success.* The more complex or lengthy the task is, the more rested and ready your child needs to be to manage it. A common example relates to homework. Often parents try to get children to tackle homework the minute they get home from school. This may not work well if the child is exhausted and overwhelmed from a full day at school.

  A better choice of timing may be to allow the child some downtime after school, and then get out the homework when the child's batteries have recharged a bit. Likewise, taking a child who is easily overwhelmed and chronically anxious to the grocery store on a Saturday morning for the major weekly shopping is probably a poor choice of timing. Probably, it will work better to make the shopping trip brief, or tackle longer shopping excursions when the store is less busy.

  The length of the activity or task is another way to adjust timing to better fit the needs of the child. It is best to continue with something only as long as the child can competently manage it. This means that you may expect your child to engage in cleaning the bedroom for 10 minutes before moving onto something else, and then coming back to the room for another 10 minutes of cleaning later on. Some children do best with very brief periods of engagement, while others can engage for longer periods.

Parents need to gauge appropriate expectations based on age, developmental level, frustration tolerance, level of fatigue, and situational factors.

Simplifying activities in terms of environment, timing, roles, and people involved is an essential component of reducing resistance, negativity, and overwhelm on the part of your child. When in doubt, it is best to simplify tasks and expectations even more than you may feel is necessary to support your child's sense of competence and keep stress levels low. Remember that complexity is in the eye of the beholder, and your perception of what is manageable may differ greatly from your child's.

When you adjust tasks and expectations to better align with your child's needs and perceptions, you show your child that you are understanding and want to ensure success. Starting simple and building from there can help tasks and activities go more smoothly, and create a stronger bond between you and your child.

TRAVIS' STORY

Travis was a five-year-old boy with significant disabilities subsequent to being born very prematurely. He was easily over stimulated, and very resistive to most tasks and activities anyone tried to do with him. Travis cried and screamed often, and generally preferred to be by himself with specific repetitive musical toys that brought him the predictability and comfort he craved. Because of his many neurological challenges, Travis struggled to make sense of the world around him; and most environments and tasks felt overwhelming to him. He lacked any sense of being able to competently engage with people and activities; and he therefore resisted most things, and preferred that others do things for him.

When I met Travis, I could tell right away that overwhelm was a major factor for him. I worked with his parents to help them understand that processing difficulties, overwhelm, and anxiety were at the root of most of the challenges they were facing with Travis each day. A key starting point was simplifying activities and environments to reduce the level of stimulation, and give Travis successful experiences with people and tasks. His parents selected Travis' bedroom as a low-stimulation area in which to engage him, as his siblings, pets, television, and other auditory and visual factors were not present.

They started with very simple roles and expectations, such as having Travis place his socks in the hamper when they got him undressed at night. Simple games such as rolling a ball back and forth, or stacking large blocks provided opportunities for Travis and his parents to engage together successfully for very brief periods of time in a non-stimulating environment. As Travis began to see that he could participate in these brief simple activities without becoming overwhelmed or anxious, he was slowly able to extend the amount of time and the complexity of activities.

His parents were able to branch out to have him do simple things with them in the kitchen and other areas of the home, always planning the activity to ensure a role, expectation, length of time, and level of stimulation that would be manageable for him. If they planned something that didn't work well, they reviewed what factors may have led to the breakdown, and then further simplified the next attempt. Simplifying activities was a key factor in building a trusting relationship between Travis and his parents, and helped him develop a better sense of competence that he could successfully participate in activities. His anxiety level went down, his engagement went up, and he was much less resistive to participate in daily tasks and activities.

Key Take-Away

Situations that are overly complex can be frustrating and create a sense of incompetence for children and parents. Simplifying activities and expectations promotes a stronger parent-child relationship, lessens resistance on the part of the child, and leads to more successful engagement.

CHAPTER 18

STOP THE ACTION

*Stopping everything, like pressing a pause button,
can more efficiently and effectively help children
and parents through challenging moments.*

Nothing is more emotionally distressing and exhausting for a parent than seeing their child become upset, scared, or angry to the point of total breakdown. Depending on the age and functioning level of the child, these breakdowns can manifest as temper tantrums, screaming, crying, hitting, kicking, running away, damaging property, verbal threats, and more. Breakdowns are a good descriptor for these episodes, as the child's ability to process information and respond appropriately is literally breaking down. Recall my earlier discussion of what happens in the brain when someone goes into fight-or-flight mode. The brain literally shuts down non-essential processes, which includes the parts of the brain responsible for rational logical thought. During these breakdown episodes children are not capable of thinking through the situation, their emotions, or their responses in an organized regulated manner.

Everyone has a certain limited capacity to cope with stressors and task demands, but when a situation exceeds the individual's capacity, functioning begins to break down. All humans experience this at various times, but the response in children tends to be more pronounced and externalized than it is for adults. It can be helpful to think of a child's coping capacity as being represented by an empty glass. Throughout the day the glass gets filled with stressors, task demands, and emotions like water getting poured into the glass. When the child experiences situations in which the water gets too close to the top of the glass, and water continues to pour in, breakdowns can happen. The child simply doesn't have the coping capacity needed to manage what is happening.

> The more calm, quiet, and in control the parent stays, the quicker the child will be able to calm and return to a more organized and rational state of functioning.

When things get really challenging and a child is breaking down, blowing up, or otherwise escalating behavior, stopping the action can be an effective solution. This goes against the instinct of most parents, which is to immediately try to do something to stop the child's behavior and distress. However, these instinctual responses of bargaining with the child, demanding the child stop, trying to force the child to do something, or threatening consequences rarely have the desired effect of calming the child and moving through the situation supportively. The opposite approach of stopping everything, like pressing a pause button, can more efficiently and effectively help children and parents through challenging moments.

Stopping the action involves the following key steps:

1. *Stay very calm throughout the episode.* When parents become agitated, anxious, and otherwise escalated with their own emotions, it continues to fuel the distress and negative reaction on the part of the child. Use deep breathing, mental distraction, or other techniques that work to help you calm and soothe your own emotional distress and anxiety during these episodes. This takes practice!

2. *Stay very quiet, and say only what absolutely needs to be said.* Inserting a lot of verbal communication into these situations is the equivalent of continuing to pour water into a cup that is already overflowing. The child is already distressed and not in a rational state of mind; so adding more verbal communication into the mix will likely serve only to make the situation worse. Use calm clear statements rather than questions, and keep your communication overall to the bare minimum. Do not yell, threaten, try to argue or negotiate or bargain with the child, as this will only create more distress and lengthen the duration of the episode.

3. *Maintain a safe physical boundary.* This may mean that the parent stays near the child to ensure he does not create a physically unsafe situation, or attempt to run from the area. If the child is threatening to run away from you, it may be appropriate to hold onto the child's hand or maintain some other physical connection with the child to ensure safety. Creating a safe or less stimulating environment may mean guiding or moving the child to a different room or location.

Depending on the circumstances, it may be necessary to remove other people or physical objects from the environment to avoid an unsafe situation. The child needs to know that you are not going to force him to do anything in that moment, but you are also not going to allow the situation to turn into a free-for-all. Children need to know that someone else is firmly in control at that moment, as that helps reduce the out-of-control feeling they are experiencing.

4. *Wait for signs that the child's fight-or-flight response is diminishing.* These signs include breathing and heart rate returning to normal, pupils becoming less dilated, muscles relaxing, verbal quieting, less physical restlessness, and more organized thought patterns. Any of the signs indicate that the child's brain is coming out of emotional mode, and back into logical/rational mode. Continue to calmly and quietly allow this recovery process to occur for the child, and do not rush too quickly to address the situation or move on to the next thing.

5. *Once the child is clearly calm and more organized in behavior and thinking, simply move on to whatever needs to come next.* Do not use this time to launch into barraging the child with questions about what happened, giving lengthy explanations about why he shouldn't have reacted that way, or reciting all the punishments and consequences that will be imposed as a result. Engaging in these responses will at best not be processed by the child, and at worst put the child right back into fight-or-flight mode, neither of which is helpful.

If there is some kind of restitution needed, such as cleaning up things that got knocked over or spilled, then calmly and quietly help the child take care of that. Otherwise, calmly direct the child to whatever needs to happen next. If there is more extensive discussion that needs to occur related to the incident, it should wait until a later time when the emotions and distress of the incident are not so fresh for parent and child.

When children become highly distressed and experience breakdowns in their functioning, it can be stressful for all involved. The more calm, quiet, and in control the parent stays, the quicker the child will be able to calm and return to a more organized and rational state of functioning. Stopping the action provides a predictable set of strategies that help support parents and children during challenging moments of dysregulated behavior. When used consistently, this approach helps children know that parents are able to handle whatever situation may arise in a way that is supportive of the child and supports, rather than erodes, the parent-child relationship.

MARNIE'S STORY

Marnie was an older teenager when I started working with her family. She had a long history of attention difficulties, impulsivity, mood disorder, and explosive behaviors. Her parents had always struggled with knowing how to deal effectively with Marnie's frequent emotional and behavioral breakdowns which consisted of extended episodes of yelling and verbally threatening them as well as herself. Occasionally, she would escalate to physically aggressive behavior including attempts to push her mother or throw things.

Over the years, they had tried strategies ranging from giving consequences to giving in to her demands; yet nothing had consistently improved her behaviors. They were appropriately concerned about how these issues were going to impact her ability to finish school, and eventually engage in life activities as an adult. Her parents were eager to help her learn the skills she needed to be independent in adulthood, yet Marnie's challenging behaviors were creating obstacles to establishing even basic expectations at home.

The treatment plan for Marnie consisted of many carefully layered interventions including nutrition and sleep supports, cognitive behavior therapy, neurofeedback, and parent training. One of the first things we needed to do was develop new patterns of behavior in the home in order to reduce the chronic episodes of behavioral escalation that were happening between Marnie and her parents. I explained the basis for the stop the action strategy to Marnie's parents, as well as the steps involved. We talked through how they would use this approach when Marnie began to emotionally and behaviorally escalate: staying very calm, limiting their verbal responses to her, refraining from asking questions or making demands, and maintaining a physically safe boundary for themselves and her.

Because she was an older teen, I also met with Marnie. Without going into details, I explained that her parents were going to be approaching these situations with her differently in an effort to help her feel better when her emotions got out of control. It was not an easy process for Marnie's parents to shift their way of responding to her during these episodes; and her father especially struggled with staying calm and not reacting to her often outrageous statements during them. With practice, they both became better able to maintain calm and composure during Marnie's flare-ups. They quickly realized that not verbally engaging with everything she said reduced the duration of her arguments and escalations.

Over time and with consistent application of the "stop the action" strategy, the parents reported a significant reduction in these breakdown episodes. While Marnie would still become resistive or upset, she was better able to engage with her parents to address the issue as opposed to completely losing control; and her parents found that they were less afraid and exhausted at having to deal with her. The relationship between Marnie and her parents began to improve as there were fewer explosive episodes, and the parents were not constantly walking on eggshells around their daughter. These changes provided an opening for her parents to begin expanding the expectations and opportunities for helping Marnie learn new skills at home.

▶ **Key Take-Away**

Intense emotionally and behaviorally charged situations can arise between parents and children with attention, anxiety, mood, and behavior challenges. When this happens, the "stop the action" strategy supports the needs of the child, reduces the duration and intensity of the child's reaction, and strengthens the connection between parent and child.

CHAPTER 19

ZONE OF CONNECTION

Many children with attention, anxiety, mood, and behavior challenges struggle to stay engaged and connected to others outside their immediate vicinity.

Zone of connection is an important concept to understand in terms of the parent-child relationship. It can be defined as the amount of space between parent and child that allows for continuous engagement and attention to one another. Newborn babies require a very close zone of connection, as they do not have any ability to make sense of the world apart from us. We hold them physically close, and gradually expand the zone of connection as they develop.

As babies grow, they develop the ability to be further from you while staying mentally connected. For example, a 10-month-old baby can sit on the floor across the room and be attentive to the fact that you are sitting on the couch near him. By the time a child reaches formal school age, you expect that the zone of connection has expanded to the point where your child can sit in a classroom and stay mentally engaged and connected to the teacher at the front of the room.

> The more hectic and overwhelming the environment, the closer the zone of connection may need to be.

While this is the typical evolution of zone of connection, many children with attention, anxiety, mood, and behavior challenges struggle to stay engaged and connected to others outside their immediate vicinity. This can especially be the case for both young and older children with more severe impairments. Those with attention difficulties may struggle to know what to attend to; and as a result, attend to whatever captures their attention or is closest to them at the moment. Those with anxiety issues may be so inwardly consumed with anxious thoughts that they are unable to stay engaged with the people and activities around them. Processing challenges also make it more difficult to stay connected across larger spaces, as there are many competing elements in the environment.

The zone of connection you need with your child will likely change depending on the context. The more hectic and overwhelming the environment, for example, the closer the zone of connection may need to be. A child who is consumed with a task such as playing a video game will likely need you to establish a close zone of connection in order to shift attention to you. That same child may be able to stay engaged with you across a wider area under other circumstances. The zone of connection can be physical as well, meaning that you have a physical connection with your child by holding hands, a shoulder touch, linking arms, etc. Children with a very difficult time attending to what is going on around them may require a physical zone of connection to stay mentally and physically engaged with the adult.

Below are specific considerations regarding the zone of connection with children:

- *It can be very frustrating for parents* when children do not seem to orient or pay attention when being spoken to. Zone of connection is a key factor in addressing this issue. You will find it is easier to gain your child's attention if you get close to your child and position yourself near their eye level. This helps the child be more aware of your presence and communication. You may take your child's hands in yours if there is a need to help your child stay close to you or remain attentive to you.

- *If your child is prone to grabbing materials or items nearby,* then maintaining a close zone of connection during games, projects, or other activities is essential. Sit near your child, ideally at a 90-degree angle, so you are able to see each other and also so that you can easily control the materials as well as establish a physical zone of connection with your child if needed.

- *Some children do not maintain an appropriate zone of connection* when walking with parents or out in public places. In these cases, a close zone of physical connection is necessary initially with the goal of slowly expanding the zone of connection so the child stays near without physical contact. Children who tend to run away from parents require a close physical zone of connection in order to learn how to stay with parents. Once this is established, parents can give the child brief opportunities to walk next to them without holding hands. The moment they begin to move too far away, the parent should reestablish the close physical zone of connection. If the child is older and resistive to holding a hand, then linking arms, keeping a hand on the child's elbow or shoulder, or holding onto an item together (i.e.: a shopping cart) is another option.

- *If your child has great difficulty knowing where his attention should be,* establish a physical zone of connection by gently taking his hand and bringing it to your face. The movement of his hand will help him orient and attend to you. This is a supportive way to assist children with cutting through the clutter in their brain to focus on one thing. It is a far better approach than moving the child's face with your hand (which no adult should ever do), verbally repeating his name, or other actions attempting to get his to shift attention to you.

- *When working on school assignments, projects, or other tasks that require sustained attention* (and may be non-preferred), keeping a closer zone of connection can be helpful. Sitting near your child, even if you are not directly working on the task, can provide a helpful reminder of where the focus should be during that time.

- *When giving instructions to your child, or making a request,* it is wise to establish a close zone of connection first. Calling out to your child to come to the dinner table may not yield results, whereas getting physically closer to your child and then telling him to come to the table will be more effective. This strategy is especially helpful if you will be instructing your child to do something that is non-preferred or potentially dysregulating for him.

Getting close first allows you to better manage the situation if the child begins to become upset or attempts to avoid the request. For some children, it is highly effective to get close to them at their eye level, take them by the hands, wait for them to shift their gaze to you, and then start your communication. This helps ensure the child is engaged and listening from the beginning, and cuts down on frustration for everyone involved.

The goal over time with any child is to expand the zone of connection so he can stay mentally connected to and engaged with others across a larger amount of space. You want to continue expanding the amount of space between you in order to stretch and strengthen awareness and attentiveness over time. This can be a slower process for some children than others. Remember that during especially stressful or challenging moments, all children require a closer zone of connection than they would under more typical circumstances. Stay aware of your child's needs in the moment, and adjust your zone of connection accordingly.

GIDEON'S STORY

Gideon was a highly active little boy who was always on the move. His parents struggled to take him anywhere, as he was constantly running from them. This would happen at home as well, particularly during transition times when they needed him to move to a different area or task. Gideon had difficulty staying focused on an activity for longer than a few moments, and was very disorganized in his use of materials. His parents would attempt to engage him in activities, but he would generally dart off after a few moments, or his attention would be consumed with something other than what they were doing.

After observing Gideon with his parents for a brief session, I could see that zone of connection was going to be a crucial component of addressing their struggles. I began by providing his parents with information about zone of connection and its importance for helping a child establish engagement and attentiveness, and then I demonstrated this approach with Gideon. I took him by the hand and led him into the observation room, which prevented him from darting away. Once in the room, we sat down to do a simple puzzle together (this was a task I knew he was capable of doing).

I sat him across from me on the floor with his back against the wall, and my legs stretched out on either side of his body to provide a clear physical boundary. The puzzle board was between us on the floor, and I kept the puzzle pieces to the side of me so he could not randomly grab them. I brought out one piece at a time for him to put in the puzzle, and sometimes I put pieces in as well.

Establishing this close zone of connection allowed Gideon to stay more engaged and attentive to me and to the task in front of us. If he attempted to get up to leave the area, I gently took his hand and waited until he sat down again. I didn't force him to sit, but I also didn't let go of his hand so he could run around the room. I instructed his parents to establish a physical zone of connection by holding his hand whenever they were transitioning from one place to another. This included situations such as when he needed to come to the table for a meal, when they took him out to a store, or when he needed to pick up a toy and place it in the toy box across the room. The initial goal was to help Gideon stay appropriately connected to parents across environments, and to improve his awareness and focus as a result.

After a few weeks of diligently establishing a close physical zone of connection with Gideon, his parents began to notice that he was not as chaotic with his movement. He initially fought holding their hands at times, but after a few weeks, was reaching for their hand before it was even offered. His parents were less exhausted, as they were not chasing Gideon around every time they needed him to go somewhere or do something. They were more effectively engaging him in simple activities without having his attention scattered between materials and other things in the environment. This focus on the zone of connection provided a foundation to begin branching out to other areas requiring intervention.

▶ **Key Take-Away**

Zone of connection is the amount of space between parent and child that allows for continuous engagement and attention to one another. Establishing the appropriate zone of connection for children allows them to stay better engaged and attentive to people and activities.

Time to Be Together

One of the best ways to strengthen the parent-child relationship, despite the challenges that may arise on a daily basis, is to simply spend time being together without specific demands. Non-demanding time means that you are not doing tasks or activities where either of you is trying to get something from the other person: you are not trying to get your child to do something, and your child is not trying to get you to do something in a specific way.

During this time, you are not engaging in tasks or activities that are challenging for either of you, nor are you trying to teach new skills. There are no phones or other devices allowed that could distract either person from the other. The goal is to just be together without expectations. Whatever does or doesn't unfold is fine, and there is no end goal to the activity.

> The reality is that all children benefit immensely from time with a parent where the focus is simply on being together without an agenda. During this time, there is no judgment and no focus on what the child is doing "right" or "wrong."

This strategy is especially helpful for children who are chronically overwhelmed and resistive to doing anything with other people. The lack of demands and expectations allows these children to experience being with a parent in a supportive way that builds competence and reduces anxiety. It is also very beneficial for parents of teenagers who can often be resistive to spending time with parents, yet need the support that comes from a strong parent-child relationship. The reality is that all children benefit immensely from time with a parent where the focus is simply on being together without an agenda. During this time, there is no judgment and no focus on what the child is doing "right" or "wrong." It is a time to simply be in each other's presence.

There are endless ways that parents and children can spend non-demanding time together. The options appropriate for you and your child will depend on personal preferences as well as your child's age, developmental level, skill levels, and personality. An appropriate non-demanding activity for one child may be very different than what is appropriate for another. Select options that you know will be non-demanding for your child, and go from there.

To start you thinking about potential ways to spend time together, below are some of the ideas families at my clinic have come up with:

- Look at picture books together
- Color a picture together (there are great coloring books available now for older children and adults, as well the traditional options for younger children)
- Lie on the ground together, and watch the clouds move across the sky
- Sit together to eat a snack together
- Play in the sandbox together
- Tear up scrap paper together
- Sing songs together
- Go for a walk together
- Go for a bike ride together
- Listen to music together
- Create something together with blocks or other building materials
- Lie in a hammock together
- Pick dandelions together
- Play together in the ball pit
- Give your child a back rub

- Take turns squishing each other with pillows
- Sit in the bathroom while your child takes a bath, and splash water together
- Do yoga poses together
- Play a simple noncompetitive game together
- Go to the lake or beach to watch the water together
- Sit in a room together and do absolutely nothing

Spending time just being with your child, without demands and expectations may be a new concept; but it can be very beneficial for strengthening relationships, reducing stress, and combating anxiety. Allow yourself and your child time to get used to it, and start with brief time periods if that is more comfortable and works better with your schedule. It is fine to start with a few minutes and build from there, as even a few minutes of non-demanding time together on a regular basis provides benefits. I encourage parents to aim for at least a few uninterrupted non-demanding time blocks with their child each week. See what benefits unfold for you and your child!

> **Key Take-Away**
> A great way for parents to strengthen the relationship with their child, reduce anxiety, and promote positive communication and relational skills is to engage in periods of uninterrupted, non-demanding time together on a regular basis.

part six: **cognition**

CHAPTER 20

LEARNING HOW TO THINK

All children, regardless of the severity of their challenges, can learn basic problem-solving skills, increase their ability to tolerate change, improve flexible thinking, and develop appropriate coping behaviors.

If you've ever told your child, "I just wish you would think for a minute before reacting!" you have experienced the frustration of engaging with someone who is not using their cognitive skills effectively in that moment. What is cognition? Cognition encompasses higher level brain functions such as attending, sequencing, prioritizing, monitoring, regulating, recalling, comprehending, problem solving, and more.

Another word for cognition is thinking, and there are often specific thinking skills that are deficient in children with attention, anxiety, mood, and behavior challenges. Specifically, these children can struggle with the cognitive skills involved in initiating tasks, thinking about things in multiple ways, coping with frustrations, managing change, tolerating mistakes,solving problems, and being aware of what is going on within and around them. These abilities require attention in order for children to regulate their behavior and emotions, as well as independently manage daily life in an ever-changing and often challenging world.

You may be thinking that you've already tried working with your child on cognitive skills but haven't gotten very far. Perhaps you have brought your child to counseling for many years to work on cognitive behavior strategies; but while your child is able to say what should be done in a certain situation, he cannot implement strategies in real life situations. I see this often in children with these challenges. It typically occurs because the strategies are taught out of context, without adequately breaking down the steps; and parents are not brought into the picture for consistent practice and implementation.

It is necessary to ensure your child has appropriate foundations for understanding and implementing cognitive strategies; and they often need to be broken down into very small components to make progress. Some children will be unable to benefit from cognitive strategies until other supports are implemented first. But all children, regardless of the severity of their challenges, can learn basic problem-solving skills, increase their ability to tolerate change, improve flexible thinking, and develop appropriate coping behaviors.

While often underappreciated and unexplored in the assessment and treatment of children with attention, anxiety, mood, and behavior symptoms, the ability to problem solve is highly connected to the ability to cope and persevere in the face of challenges and setbacks. Poor cognitive flexibility and problem-solving skills are often at the root of the following issues:

- Overdependence on others to make decisions, or do things for them
- Low motivation and lack of initiative
- Reactive behavior such as crying, yelling, panic, aggression, or other types of break down responses
- Low self-esteem, and persistent negative outlook and self-talk
- Poor frustration tolerance, and tendency to give up on things easily
- Rigid thinking, and intolerance for change
- Fear of making mistakes
- Limited awareness of their own feelings, thoughts and behaviors
- Threats of harm to themselves, and comments such as "I'd be better off dead" when they encounter situations that don't go as planned or that they are unsure how to handle

Children exhibiting these kinds of difficulties need explicit modeling, instruction, and guidance to develop appropriate flexible thinking and problem-solving skills. There are many options available, and the following pages provide some simple starting points for addressing problem-solving deficits in children. Choose the solutions that make the most sense for your child based on age, level of functioning, and coping ability.

No matter the age of your child, it is never too late to begin addressing these issues. I've worked with parents of children in their 20s and beyond who were finally able to help their children make progress in these areas when provided with the proper solutions. Remember to start small, and gradually increase expectations and challenges as your child can tolerate. These tools will give you the knowledge and guidance you need as a parent to begin improving these critical skills for your child.

Thinking Without Prompting

As a parent, you may find yourself giving your child constant reminders, telling them what to do, and sometimes physically moving them through tasks that need to get done. A prompt is a cue, trigger or reminder that is given in order to elicit a specific response from someone. When you tell your child to "hurry up," you are prompting him to move faster with whatever he is doing. Picking up the pencil and handing it to the child may be a prompt to get started on the worksheet in front of him. Saying, "I didn't hear the toilet flush" is a prompt to flush the toilet. You prompt others often, and in various ways—especially children.

Parental prompting can be problematic because it essentially puts adults in the role of thinking and problem solving.

Common examples of prompts adults use with children include verbal directions, verbal reminders, physical guiding, pointing, and demonstrating. Parents may prompt a child to put his dishes in the sink by telling him to do it, handing them the dirty dishes, or making a comment like, "Those dishes won't put themselves in the sink." There are different types of prompts you can give: direct or indirect, verbal or nonverbal.

Parental prompting can be problematic because it essentially puts adults in the role of thinking and problem solving, and children in the role of merely following directions. Children who are frequently prompted to do things can develop prompt dependence, rarely thinking about or taking action on something without an external prompt. Instead, they wait until someone else tells them what to do before thinking or acting.

This can happen with any child, but it is prevalent in children with attention, anxiety, mood, and behavior challenges. These children sometimes struggle to think about things, or determine what they should do on their own; and adults often jump in rather quickly to tell them what to do. As a result, children learn that someone else will usually do their thinking and problem solving for them. Over time, children just default to waiting for prompts rather than initiating their own thinking and problem solving first.

> Children who are frequently prompted to do things can develop prompt dependence, rarely thinking about or taking action on something without an external prompt.

Consider the following scenarios:

- *Evan never takes his morning vitamins* until his mother verbally reminds him at least three times and places the vitamins directly in front of him at the table.

- *Tonya leaves her dirty clothes and towel strewn on the bathroom floor,* and doesn't take care of them until explicitly told to do so by her parents.

- *When working on homework, Jeremy does one problem and then stops* until his father tells him to keep going with the next problem.

- *Levi stuffs all his papers in his folder* each day unless his mother specifically tells him where each one needs to go.

- *Vanessa passively sits and does nothing* unless someone directly tells her what to do next.

In each of these situations, the child has fallen into a pattern of waiting for explicit cues or instructions from adults before taking action. While parents can continue to prompt their children in these ways, there is no progression toward independent thinking and action. Without shifting strategies, the adult remains in the position of monitoring and figuring out what needs to happen; and the child simply waits to be told what to do. You must think about prompting differently in order to promote problem-solving and thinking skills in your children.

No matter the age or functioning level of your child, the goal should be to utilize prompts in a way that promotes as much mental engagement as possible on the part of your child.

It is important to be mindful of creating opportunities for children to think about what they need to do and then take action. Many children need adults to structure this process for them in a way that encourages thinking but provides enough support to be successful. The chart below provides a sample sequence of prompting levels that can be used to support any child through this thinking and problem-solving process. The goal is to start with the least specific prompt and move down the list to more direct prompts only if necessary. This same procedure should be used as often as possible when situations arise, starting at the top with the least directive prompt, and working your way down the list until the child is able to respond.

Do not fall into the trap of assuming your child will not benefit from or respond to a less directive prompt. Over time, you should not need to go as far down the list because the child will be doing more thinking in response to less directive prompts. The goal with any child should be to first reduce the level of directness that is needed for the child to respond, and then reduce the amount of prompting overall.

No matter the age or functioning level of your child, the goal should be to utilize prompts in a way to promote as much mental engagement as possible on the part of your child. It is helpful to become aware of how often you are directly prompting your child, and then start to shift to less frequent or directive prompts. Keep in mind that your child may not respond immediately, and you will likely need to wait expectantly for him to think through the situation and take action.

I encourage you to hold out for a response of some kind from your child before jumping in, as many children default to just waiting for an adult to do things for them or at least give another reminder. If your child is already quite prompt dependent, you will likely need to wait longer for a response, as the child will be expecting you to just take care of things or lead them through it. Start thinking about small ways you can prompt less or in a different way, and build up from there. The result will be a child who has better awareness, is more attentive, and initiates actions and solutions without constantly needing adult intervention or explicit instruction.

Type of Prompt (in order from least directive to most directive)	Examples
1. Verbal comment about the situation	"It looks like there's a problem with the dishes."
	"I've got my coat on and am ready to go outside."
	"I haven't noticed you doing your laundry for more than a week."
2. Indirect verbal prompt to think about possible solutions/actions	"I wonder what you might do about those dishes sitting there."
	"I bet you're going to need your coat, too."
	"It looks like you might need to look at your laundry situation."
3. Verbalize a solution you might use	"If my dirty dishes had been sitting on the table all day, I would put them in the sink."
	"If I saw people waiting for me with their coats on, I'd get my coat on, too."
	"If I didn't have any clean socks left, I would do my laundry."
4. Ask the child to choose between two solutions	"Are you going to bring your dishes to the sink by yourself, or should you and I do it together?"
	"Are you going to put on this red coat or this black jacket?"
	"Will you be doing your laundry now or after dinner?"
5. Model/demonstrate for the child (make sure you have child's attention by moving closer, getting on the child's level, etc.)	Bring your own dirty dishes to the sink.
	Put on your coat.
	Begin putting child's dirty laundry in the basket.

Type of Prompt (in order from least directive to most directive)	Examples
6. Direct nonverbal prompt (make sure you have child's attention by moving closer, getting on the child's level, etc.)	Point to the dirty dishes and then to the sink. Hold the coat out to the child. Hand the child an empty laundry basket.
7. Direct verbal prompt with nonverbal cue	"Put the dishes in the sink." + point to sink "Put this coat on." + point to/hand coat "Do your laundry now." + hand empty basket

> ▶ **Key Take-Away**
>
> Constant direct prompting, such as repeated verbal reminders or telling your child what to do can create prompt dependence. This reduces opportunities for children to grow in their ability to think and problem solve independently.

CHAPTER 21

IMPROVING FLEXIBILITY & COPING SKILLS

Change creates uncertainty and requires aditional effort to make sense of new information.

There is a famous thought attributed to Heraclitus that "the only thing constant is change." If you try to think of the last time your day went exactly as planned, you realize how true that observation is. While you are always planning for certain things, there is rarely a time when everything goes exactly as you anticipate. Regardless of how tightly you attempt to plan your lives, changes arise that require adaptation. Change comes up regularly, and you require flexible thinking to adapt and adjust your plans to still meet your obligations and goals.

Flexible thinking is the ability to think about something in multiple ways, adapt to new situations, come up with multiple ways to solve problems, and improvise when needed. Many children with attention, anxiety, mood, and behavior challenges struggle with flexible thinking. This can result in a child who gets stuck in one way of thinking about or doing something. It can also cause children to struggle with coming up with new ways to address problems or challenges when "plan A" doesn't work out. Children with weak flexible thinking skills tend to prefer routines, and can become upset and dysregulated when predictable patterns are altered.

There are some specific reasons that children with developmental and mental health issues struggle with poor flexible thinking skills. They often have processing difficulties that impact their ability to keep pace with activities and expectations. When a child has difficulty quickly and efficiently making sense of things, it is easier to manage when situations stay the same. The more change there is, the more difficult it is to keep up with taking in, making sense of and responding to information.

Change requires additional effort to make sense of new information; and that can be a slow frustrating process for some children, especially when the expectation is for them to think and respond quickly. Another issue can be anxiety and avoidance of uncertainty. The more predictable and routine things remain, the less anxiety provoking they are. Changes create uncertainty as the child is not sure exactly what will happen during or following the event. As their anxiety increases, children may attempt to calm themselves by resisting change.

When a child has weak flexible thinking skills, it is essential to provide them opportunities to notice new information and changes, and develop strategies to adapt. By creating small moments throughout the day when children experience something unexpected, we can provide them with flexible thinking practice. Many parents are hesitant to intentionally create any changes for their child, as he becomes so anxious and upset by it.

The key to this strategy is to create moments of uncertainty that do not overwhelm your child, such that he can learn to think through and cope with them successfully. Each child has a different capacity for managing change; if pushed too far, they will become confused, frustrated, overwhelmed, and resistive. It is important for parents to take their child's tolerance for uncertainty and level of rigidity into account when designing experiences that promote flexible thinking. Some children require small changes introduced slowly over time in order to manage them successfully. Others can manage larger more frequent changes.

> Flexible thinking is the ability to think about something in multiple ways, adapt to new situations, come up with multiple ways to solve problems, and improvise when needed.

The basic steps for helping a child build a foundation for flexible thinking skills and increased tolerance for change are below. This process can be used for children of any age or functioning level, and can be used to address virtually any rigid thought process or behavioral pattern:

1. *Identify a routine or situation that is well established for your child.* It can be something as simple as the toothpaste always being in the top drawer of the bathroom vanity, or something more involved such as the routine for getting ready for bed.

2. *Select one aspect of the routine or situation to change.* The toothpaste tube may be out on the counter instead of in the drawer. In the case of the bedtime routine, you may decide to lay your child's pajamas out on the bedroom floor instead of in the bathroom. You are looking to identify a change that will be noticeable to your child without being completely overwhelming. Choose something that seems like a good starting point.

3. *Implement the change, and note your child's response.* If your child doesn't even notice the change, it was too small and you will want to select a slightly more noticeable difference next time. If your child was completely overwhelmed and dysregulated by the change (tantrums, screaming, refusal to continue engagement in the task, etc.), then the change was too big, and you will want to select a smaller change the next time.

    If your child noticed the change but was not overwhelmed or highly distressed, and was able to continue participation in the task or process, then this is an excellent starting point. Your child's response is the barometer for determining whether you need to back up to a smaller change, speed up to a larger one, or have selected the "just right" starting point.

4. *Once you've found an initial change that is noticeable* and tolerable, continue making additional changes from that point. In the case of the toothpaste, you may move a variety of items around in the bathroom over the course of days or weeks. The bedtime routine may be altered in the order of tasks, which parent helps the child with which tasks,

where certain parts of the routine take place, etc. Proceed with layers of change over time until the child is flexible with all aspects of the routine or situation.

Remember that helping your child become more comfortable with change is a process, and your child is not always going to be comfortable. You are not looking for your child to be happy about the changes you make. Rather, you are working on finding the level of change that is not completely overwhelming or paralyzing. A child may notice and express frustration or disagreement with it. If he is still able to manage the situation despite this change, however, then it will strengthen flexible thinking.

When a child is so distressed by change that he becomes highly upset or enraged, there is no opportunity for positively impacting thinking skills. Work to find the balance between not stretching your child's flexibility skills at all, and stretching them too far to the point of breaking. It is a process, and one that you may find yourself reevaluating regularly. Keep trying, and know that you will eventually find the sweet spot starting point where your child notices and can manage the change without falling apart. From that point on, continue stretching them slowly forward with bigger and more frequent changes.

> Young children who are extremely rigid grow into older children and young adults who are extremely rigid. It generally gets worse over time if not addressed, and leads to both children and parents living in an irrational prison of rigid thinking and behavior.

These strategies are especially important for children who become highly fixated on certain routines and patterns and may attempt to get adults to respond in specific ways. Examples include the child who wants his mother to say "goodnight, sleepy head" every night before bed, who insists that food is served only on a specific plate, who will only eat brand specific foods prepared in very specific ways, or who becomes upset when you drive a different route to get to school. These children have severe deficits in flexible thinking, and require consistent work in this area to become more comfortable and competent with change.

While parents may feel it makes life easier to just succumb to the child's rigid demands, over time this is the most exhausting and difficult path to take. Young children who are extremely rigid grow into older children and young adults who are extremely rigid. It generally gets worse over time if not addressed, and leads to both children and parents living in an irrational prison of rigid thinking and behavior. No one is happy or competent in that scenario, and it does not lead a child down the path of productive relational or work skills later in life.

Children with poor flexible thinking skills can develop rigid ways of managing change and uncertainty. It is important for parents to support the development of greater flexibility so that the child does not continue living in fear, and can learn to tolerate and even enjoy new and different experiences. Start small and build from there, keeping in mind that the more impaired and/or anxious the child, the slower the process should be. Addressing the issue in this way allows children to not just be compliant with change, but actually become comfortable with it.

ELENA'S STORY

Elena was a highly anxious eight year old when I first met her. She had very rigid preferences for routines and environments, including foods. Her parents were highly concerned about her food intake, as she was only eating five foods consistently; and they were all brand and presentation specific. For example, Elena would eat Ritz brand crackers with smooth Jif™ peanut butter spread on the non-salt side. If any variations were made to the crackers and peanut butter, she would not eat them.

She was being carefully monitored by her physician in regard to weight loss and growth, and had been to numerous feeding clinics and other therapies in an attempt to increase her food intake. Her parents reported that each therapy had resulted in Elena dropping more foods from her diet, as she would become so fearful and upset by the changes forced upon her during sessions that she would stop eating those foods altogether.

Elena was not growing and developing appropriately, and anxiety was taking over her life and her parents' lives. I could see that there were many things she would benefit from in terms of treatment in order to reduce anxiety and support her development; and strategies such as nutritional supplementation, improving sleep, neurofeedback, and parent training were all necessary. In the realm of food, we worked on building trust with her by making extremely small changes initially.

She ate Hunt's brand chocolate pudding in the plastic cups with the lid still attached to the container. We started making very tiny changes to how far the lid was pulled back on the cup. Elena was aware we were making the change with the lid and was nervous about it, but would still eat the pudding. We then moved to having her pull the lid further and further until she was able to pull the lid off the container and still eat the pudding. The next step was to place the plastic pudding cup in a bowl for her to eat it that way, which then turned into placing the plastic cup on its side in the bowl.

The process continued to move forward with her becoming able to eat the chocolate pudding out of the bowl instead of the cup, then using different kinds of utensils and bowls, and then expanding to different brands of pudding. It was a slow and tedious process, but one that allowed Elena to trust that no one was going to radically change her foods and throw her into a panic. As she became comfortable with each small change, she was strengthening her flexible thinking skills and tolerance for change. She was not merely being compliant with the changes, but was comfortable with them and able to handle them without breaking down.

As her tolerance for small changes increased, we were able to more quickly make additional changes; and the changes became bigger over time. During this time I also had parents making changes to non-food routines in the home environment, such as rotating where the kids sat in their car, making alterations to the order of the bedtime routine, and putting items in unexpected places. Anytime Elena became highly upset by a change, her parents simply went back to the previous established pattern and made a smaller change on the next attempt. They persevered and did not stop making changes altogether when she became upset. Rather, they recognized they had pushed her a bit too far and regrouped to try again.

It took about two years for Elena to become a comfortable and competent eater, meaning she was no longer chronically anxious around food, could eat at least 30 different foods, was not brand or presentation specific, and could eat food at restaurants or friend's homes without panic. She will never be the world's most adventurous eater; but she is no longer living in constant fear about food and eating. Her parents no longer need to bring bags of her specific foods with them wherever they go, and the entire family is more relaxed as a result of not fearing Elena's response to food.

> **▶ Key Take-Away**
>
> Children with rigid inflexible thinking and behavior have weak flexible thinking skills. Implementing a consistent process for helping them become more comfortable with change in routines and environments is necessary to reduce anxiety, and improve tolerance for change.

Coping with Mistakes

One of the cognitive issues that can arise for children with attention, anxiety, mood, and behavior issues is difficulty coping with mistakes or being "wrong." Some children can't stand even the possibility that they may make a mistake or do something the wrong way; and the mere idea that they could "mess up" can cause refusal or panic obsessive perfectionistic behaviors. These children can become locked in a world of absolutes where imperfection cannot be tolerated, and they resist and avoid as a result. They perceive there is a definitive "right" and "wrong" to everything, and any argument to the contrary can lead to arguing and upset. Consider the following ways this issue can manifest itself:

- *Spending most of the time on assignments* writing, erasing, and rewriting letters or numbers until they look "perfect"

- *Becoming deeply upset and argumentative* when told they are incorrect or misunderstood something

- *Refusing to complete tasks* due to fear of doing something incorrectly, or not having time to complete it perfectly

- *Working on homework assignments* long beyond the time that is necessary, in order to get each and every problem "just right"

- *Avoiding participation in games* they do not feel they can win, and being a very poor loser when a game or activity doesn't go their way

- *Waiting for an adult* to specifically tell them what to do or do something for them, in order to avoid trying on their own and possibly making an error

One way to effectively diffuse the intensity of emotion that many of these children feel about "making mistakes" is to provide them consistent exposure to mistakes in safe and controlled ways.

Children who exhibit these issues have what could be called "perfection complexes." They have one specific vision for how things should be done and how the final product should look, and they lack any tolerance for variations from this ideal. Some of them become terribly self-deprecating as a result of feeling like they can never measure up to their vision of perfection when it comes to tasks and expectations.

The above scenarios represent the kinds of issues surrounding inflexible and perfectionist thinking. Each present significant obstacles to success in life, and lead to poor self-esteem, resilience and coping skills. Inadequate flexible thinking skills are at the root of these issues, as the child is unable to think flexibly and appraise situations to determine the degree of accuracy or level of "perfection" that is required. While there are many foundational components of a child's development that must be tackled in order to deal with these obstacles completely, there are some practical strategies that can be used to help address them.

One way to effectively diffuse the intensity of emotion that many of these children feel about "making mistakes" is to provide them consistent exposure to mistakes in safe and controlled ways. The goal is for mistakes to become a normal part of what happens in any given situation rather than the exception that causes feelings of panic and shame. This can be accomplished by providing real life experiences in which making mistakes is part of the expectation, where one would be making a mistake by **not** making any mistakes, or by modeling mistakes, and talking through the process of coping with them.

Below are some specific ways to move your child toward greater understanding and acceptance of mistakes:

- *Engage in activities where the goal is to make mistakes on purpose.* This can take a variety of forms, but it is wise to start in the context of simple games or tasks such as tossing a ball to one another, tossing beanbags at large targets, or walking on a thick line of tape across the floor. Aim to start with something simple that does not require a lot of thinking on the part of the child. First, play the game the "right way": catching the ball when it's thrown; hitting the target; or walking on the line.

  At some point, stop the game to tell your child that the goal is now make mistakes as you play. You will begin missing the ball, missing the target, walking off the line, etc. Making this modification allows the child to experience "making mistakes" in a structured way, and provides the opportunity for positive experiences related to them.

- *Apply this same concept of "purposeful mistakes" to other tasks at home.* For example, ask your child to write a sentence and make at least three mistakes with spelling, punctuation, etc. Have your child sort the dirty laundry, and mistakenly hide one or two "wrong" color items in the basket for you to find before washing. Cook together, and have them try to spill something like salt or water while measuring. Have your child write down five facts about their favorite animal, including one thing that isn't true, and then have family members try to guess the one that is wrong.

  The goal here is to help children practice making mistakes in controlled situations where they can increase their comfort level doing something the "wrong way."

- *Model your own thought process related to making mistakes.* Talk out loud as you experience mistakes or challenges so your child can benefit from hearing your thought process about it, and how you cope with it. Examples:

  Oh no! I spilled my coffee on the counter. No big deal. I'll just get a paper towel and wipe it up.

  Ugh, I turned the wrong way. Let me think about how I can get back to the street we were on. If I turn this way, I can get back over there. Yes, that will work out just fine.

  I forgot we were supposed to go to Grandma's house for dinner. It's okay, I'll just call her and let her know we will be a few minutes late. She won't be upset, and she will be glad I called to tell her.

- *Institute a daily or weekly family routine,* perhaps at dinnertime, where everyone takes a turn sharing one mistake they made that day/week. This normalizes making mistakes, and helps the child see that everyone makes them and is able to move on and even learn from them.

- *Play a game called "spot the mistake"* where your child looks for the mistakes you are making during a task or game. Allowing your child to spotlight the mistakes of others highlights that everyone makes mistakes, and also models not getting upset every time a mistake occurs.

- *Be very aware of the language you use with your child around making mistakes.* Do not embarrasses children, or make them feel ashamed or "bad" for making an error. Instead, use positive phrasing such as "It's great that you made a mistake because now we can learn something new!" If your child is highly sensitive to criticism or being told that something was done incorrectly, try saying something like, "Let's figure out if there is another way to do this."

- *If your child is prone to avoiding any independent effort* because he is waiting for you to direct the process to avoid errors or problems, set the expectation that he does something first before you assist him. Have him make some kind of effort before you provide direction or feedback, whether it is doing the first problem on a worksheet or putting the first dish in the dishwasher. This helps break the pattern of avoidance because of fear that he will make a mistake.

These activities and methods of modeling allow children to experience mistakes in a positive way, rather than negatively. They also encourage a greater comfort level with the idea of making mistakes, and allow children to realize mistakes happen to everyone, and the world goes on as usual when these things occur. Finally, implementing these strategies helps to blur the lines between what is "right" and what is "wrong," thus strengthening flexible thinking skills.

JOSEPH'S STORY

Joseph was 12-years-old and was terrified of making mistakes. He had issues with language comprehension and sensory processing that frequently made it difficult for him to understand tasks and assignments at home and school. Because he knew he may not understand something correctly, he was constantly fearful of being wrong or making an error.

He was chronically stressed at school, and would avoid initiating anything on his own out of fear that a mistake would occur. When given an assignment, he would do nothing until an adult told him exactly what to do or sat down to do it with him. He never raised his hand or spoke up in class, out of fear that he would be wrong.

The situation was the same at home where Joseph would attempt to avoid any and all situations where he might make a mistake. While he exhibited more internalizing and passive behavior at school, he would react in more externalizing ways at home including yelling, running to his bedroom, or pounding the table when he was frustrated due to errors or the thought that he might make a mistake.

After helping his mother understand why this was occurring, we began to work on ways to normalize mistakes for Joseph by having him practice with mistakes that did not have consequences in controlled settings. His mother began to engage him in more tasks with her around the house, and modeled her own thought process about the mistakes and challenges that arose. When working on homework, she would sit with him but require that he take some action on his own, however small, before she provided guidance or suggestions.

> "I hope we make a mistake, so I can learn something from it."

They practiced *making mistakes* such as missing the basket when shooting hoops in the driveway, and spelling things wrong when making lists. His mother developed specific phrases she would use with Joseph such as "No big deal" and "I hope we make a mistake, so I can learn something from it." She began congratulating him when he brought home assignments with errors, and also had him tally the number of mistakes she made when completing tasks.

These strategies were incorporated into daily life activities as much as possible to avoid it becoming a time-intensive process. As he was exposed to these activities and situations, Joseph's tolerance for mistakes and the possibility of errors increased. He began to be able to laugh at mistakes his mother made, and was tolerating his own mistakes without blowing up. His mother noted that he was more relaxed overall, and could stick with assignments and tasks longer without giving up every time a mistake occurred.

We also incorporated other strategies into Joseph's treatment plan including parent training, nutritional changes and mindfulness activities to reduce anxiety and improve coping skills. In addition to reducing anxiety and stress, his improved tolerance for mistakes allowed him to participate more actively in learning opportunities at home and school.

> ▶ **Key Take-Away**
> Understanding that mistakes are expected and manageable is essential for children to develop positive self-esteem and appropriate coping skills.

Improving Frustration Tolerance

Human beings experience frustration in all aspects of life, as it can arise anytime something does not immediately go the way you desire or expect. As adults, you may have experienced frustration with people at work who do not show up on time, or fail to complete their work in a timely manner. At home you may have experienced frustration when dinner doesn't finish cooking on time, or when your children are taking longer than necessary to get ready for bed.

Frustration is an internal tension that arises between how you want things to be and how they actually are. When you experience frustration, your instinct is to alleviate that tension as quickly as possible. People with less tolerance for frustration will immediately try to take action to reduce the tension and discomfort, while people with a higher frustration tolerance can persevere in a situation for longer periods of time without acting on their frustration. Your ability to continue engaging in or pursuing something even when the tension you feel is uncomfortable or distressing is called frustration tolerance.

Those with higher frustration tolerance have the ability to push through the discomfort in order to reach a goal or benefit on the other side, whereas individuals with lower frustration tolerance tend to prioritize their immediate comfort over any potential long-term benefit.

> Improving frustration tolerance is necessary for these children to learn how to persevere in the face of challenges.

Most children with attention, anxiety, mood, and behavior challenges have low frustration tolerance. They become easily upset when something doesn't go exactly as planned, when they encounter disappointment, feel bored, or can't make something work right away. Behaviors resulting from poor frustration tolerance can include giving up quickly, avoidance of non-preferred tasks and situations, crying and aggression, among others.

Improving frustration tolerance is necessary for these children to learn how to persevere in the face of challenges, and to better regulate their emotions and associated behavioral responses. There are numerous strategies parents can implement to improve a child's tolerance for frustration, including the following:

- *Slowly stretch your child's tolerance for uncomfortable emotions.* Be aware of your child's emotions during activities, and notice when he begins to appear frustrated, bored or upset. Extend the task or expectation only briefly beyond this point in order to slightly stretch his ability to stick with something, even though he feels frustrated or upset by it.

  If you are playing a board game, and the child is becoming frustrated or bored partway through, set the expectation that you will take just two more turns and then set the game aside for a while. This helps to extend his frustration tolerance slightly beyond the current level, without pushing him into full-blown upset or dysregulation.

Regardless of your child's age or functioning level, the goal is to slowly extend the time spent on frustrating activity just beyond the initial point of frustration before allowing him to do something else. This allows children to feel the frustration, but also to see that they can persevere despite that feeling. If you allow the frustration to go on for too long, however, children will become increasingly dysregulated and resist or give up, neither of which supports the development of improved frustration tolerance.

Over time, you can push your child to participate for longer periods as his tolerance for frustration increases and he can extend his engagement beyond the initial point of frustration.

• *Use language that encourages effort rather than outcome.* The language you use around a child's task engagement and efforts can also serve to improve frustration tolerance. You will want to praise your child's effort rather than just the outcome. A child with low frustration tolerance may struggle to bring most tasks to completion without experiencing frustration at some point in the process.

Rather than focus on the finished product, highlight the effort they put into it by making comments such as, "You worked so hard to get those last few problems done," or "I know it was really tough to make yourself finish those last few pieces, but you did it!" This helps the child understand the value of his effort to push forward despite frustration, and also lets him know that you value those efforts more highly than whatever the outcome may be.

> Allowing the child to give up on the task or activity promotes avoidance as a strategy for managing frustration, which is not beneficial for the development of frustration tolerance.

- *Teach the process of taking breaks and then returning to the challenging situation.* Many children benefit from taking breaks during difficult or frustrating tasks and activities. Breaks allow them to shift their mind to something else, move their body, and otherwise reduce their overall level of frustration and negative emotion.

  Most children do not identify that they would benefit from a break, and therefore require guidance from parents to do so when the parent becomes aware that frustration is building. If breaks are used to help the child manage frustration, it is essential that he return to the task or activity that caused the frustration in order to continue working through it.

  Allowing the child to give up on the task or activity promotes avoidance as a strategy for managing frustration, which is not beneficial for the development of frustration tolerance. Some children may need to tackle tasks in very small chunks to prevent pushing their frustration level too far in one sitting.

  As a result, these children will need to come back to the task multiple times before completing it. This helps them learn that regulating their emotions is more important than quickly finishing the task, but also instills the understanding that they need to continue working at something over time without abandoning it altogether.

▶ **Key Take-Away**

Children with attention, anxiety, mood, and behavior challenges tend to have low frustration tolerance that can lead to poor emotional and behavioral regulation. Using strategies to improve frustration tolerance allows children to persevere in the face of challenging or uncomfortable situations.

CHAPTER 22

PROBLEM SOLVING

It is essential for children to have opportunities to develop problem-solving skills and the coping abilities that come along with them.

When children encounter problems and challenges, your first instinct as parents can be to rescue them from the situation or save them from having to experience hardship or pain. While it is understandable that you do not want your children to struggle, the reality is that a certain amount of difficulty and challenge is essential for growth and development.

Children whose parents jump in to solve every problem or manage every challenge fail to develop the problem-solving skills and personal resilience they need to manage life independently. They are likely to become dependent on caregivers to make decisions for them, and tend to fall apart whenever problems arise that they cannot quickly and easily solve. This does not just happen for children with more significant impairments. I am seeing a large increase in the number of young adults who fail to successfully transition into adulthood as a result of their poor problem-solving skills and related lack of emotional resilience. It is essential for children to have opportunities to develop problem-solving skills and the coping abilities that come along with them.

There are a variety of ways to work on problem-solving skills, and many opportunities that arise over the course of everyday life. While there are certainly many natural problems that arise throughout the day, parents may also want to create specific situations where problems come up so their children have an opportunity to solve them. It is essential that you commit to allowing your child to experience the problem and participate in solving it, and not jump in to rescue.

While it is understandable that you do not want your children to struggle, the reality is that a certain amount of difficulty and challenge is essential for growth and development. Children whose parents jump in to solve every problem or manage every challenge fail to develop the problem-solving skills and personal resilience they need to manage life independently.

There is a general process you use to solve problems when they arise. While you may not be conscious of this process, particularly for minor problems or issues you encounter regularly, you still use the same basic steps to work through any problematic or challenging situation. Here is a summary of that process:

1. Recognize that a problem has occurred

2. Recognize that the problem is solvable

3. *Develop a way to solve the problem* and implement the solution

4. *Assess whether the solution worked*

5. *Come up with another solution* (plan B) if needed; return to step 4

6. *Encode the experience in memory* for use next time a similar situation occurs

Depending on the nature of the problem, children may be able to solve it on their own or may require assistance. Children with attention, anxiety, mood, and behavior challenges tend to need more support and guidance, at least initially, even with problems you may perceive as simple to solve. Remember that your goal is to engage your child in the process of addressing the problem with you, and not to do it for him. Here is an example of how this process might work for a relatively simple problem such as a spilled glass of water:

1. *Recognize that a problem has occurred:* "I see that you have a problem. Your glass of water spilled."

2. *Recognize that the problem is solvable:* "That happens sometimes, and it's a solvable problem."

3. *Develop a way to solve the problem and implement the solution:* "Let's see what ideas we can come up with to solve this. I bet you can think of something."

4. *Assess whether the solution worked:* "You got a napkin to clean it up, which was a great idea. It looks like the napkin is really wet, and there is still a lot of water on the floor."

5. *Come up with another solution–Plan B:* "I wonder what other solutions we can think of to get the floor dry."

6. *Assess whether the solution worked:* "That towel you used really did the trick, and now the floor is dry."

7. *Encode the experience in memory:* "Now you know that if you spill water on the floor, a thick towel cleans it up really well."

Some children struggle greatly with generating solutions on their own. If this is the case for your child, you can offer some potential solutions as needed. If your child was unable to offer any solutions at step three in the case of the spilled water example, you could say that "Sometimes I use a towel from the bathroom if I have a big spill, or I will get a lot of paper towels to dry it up."

This supports your child by offering solutions for them to choose from, without directly telling them what to do. Helping them generate solutions is important, especially if it is a situation your child has not encountered previously or they are really upset about the situation and cannot think through the possibilities.

Just like any other skill, the best way to improve is to practice. Children who never solve problems cannot become competent problem solvers. Parents should aim to provide opportunities for problem solving as often as possible throughout the day. There are endless possibilities, and it is typically the case that problems arise over the course of a day without parents needing to intentionally create them. Being aware of these natural opportunities allows you to capitalize on them by supporting your child through the problem-solving process.

The following situations can provide excellent opportunities for your child to practice thinking through and solving problems, with or without your guidance:

- *Something breaks* and needs to be repaired
- *A piece doesn't fit quite right* in the puzzle, or is missing from the box
- *A mess is made* and needs to be cleaned up
- *The bag of pretzels* your child usually has after school is empty
- *Your child waited until the last minute* to work on a project, and can't get it completed on time
- *Your child left lunch on the counter* at home instead of bringing it to school
- *The red crayon* your child is looking for is nowhere to be found
- *There is a food stain* on the shirt your child was going to wear to school
- *Your child didn't do laundry for three weeks,* and has no clean clothes left to wear
- *Your child wants to go for a bike ride* but the tire is flat
- *You son wants to watch one show,* but your daughter wants to watch a different one
- *Your child doesn't know how to do a problem* on the math worksheet brought home
- *The lid on the jar of peanut butter* is stuck
- *Your child didn't get up with the alarm,* and missed the bus
- *Your child went online to register for classes*, and two selections were already full

Children who never have to solve problems cannot become competent problem solvers.

There is no end to the number of problem-solving opportunities that can arise over the course of a day, as problems are a normal and expected part of daily life. Be intentional about resisting the urge to solve problems for your child when they arise, and instead guide them through the process of problem solving. While this may entail more time and emotion in the short-term, it is part of setting your child up for success over the long-term.

TREY'S STORY

Trey was 20 years old when he came to my office with his mother for an intake appointment. He had begun experiencing challenges with inattention and anxiety in middle school following a traumatic family experience, and treatment (including medication) had thus far been ineffective for improving these issues. In fact, over time his anxiety symptoms had been worsening; Trey had defaulted to increasingly passive patterns of functioning in all aspects of life. He had managed to graduate from high school because his mother continually stepped in to work with school professionals, and monitored Trey continuously to get requirements completed.

Eventually, he got an entry-level job following high school because a family member owned the company and gave him a position. At home, Trey did very little and defaulted to his mother and sister to solve every problem that arose. When his hair got too long, his mother would make an appointment for him to get it cut. If he had car trouble and couldn't make it to work on time, a family member would call his employer saying he would be late. When a check bounced at the bank, his mother would put money in his account to rectify the situation. She did his laundry to avoid the problem of him running out of clean work uniforms.

While he was chronologically 20 years old, Trey had defaulted to acting like a young child from the standpoint of solving any problems that arose in his life. This had created a situation where he was dependent on others, despite having the capability to function independently. He had very poor self-esteem, and lacked a sense of personal responsibility. There were multiple interventions that supported symptom improvement for Trey including parent training, diet changes, sleep support, exercise, and working with his prescriber to eliminate medications that were increasing his anxiety, brain fog, and irritability.

These solutions were phased in over time as he was willing and able to implement them. One of the first steps was working with his family to engage Trey in solving his own problems. I helped his mother understand why it was so important for Trey to solve problems that arose in his life, and how to provide support by guiding him rather than doing things for him. She agreed to start allowing him to deal with small problems that came up such as making sure his thermos for work was clean each morning, and replacing his personal hygiene products when they were empty. If Trey didn't clean out his thermos at night, then he needed to solve that problem in the morning. When his shampoo ran out, he needed to solve that problem by either asking his mother to buy him more or going to the store to get it himself.

> The biggest change was his mother being able to step aside and allow Trey to encounter and wrestle with challenges without rescuing him.

Once these smaller problem-solving opportunities were well established, we moved on to no longer making phone calls for him. When Trey encountered situations where a phone call was needed, such as scheduling an appointment, his mother would help him think about what to say, but she would not pick up the phone to make the call for him. If he refused to make the call, then he experienced the consequences of that. I also requested that she stop doing his laundry, and I worked with Trey to develop a schedule and process for managing that on his own. When he chose not to manage his laundry responsibly, he encountered the natural consequences of that choice.

The expectations his mother and I set for him were all very reasonable, and within the realm of his capabilities. We started with basic problems he had the skills to manage with support, and increased the expectations from there. The biggest change was his mother being able to step aside and allow Trey to encounter and wrestle with challenges without rescuing him. This was difficult for both of them initially, but over time it became the natural way she operated with him.

A few months after implementing these strategies, Trey acknowledged that he was beginning to feel better about himself and that it actually felt good to not rely on his mother so much. He was on his way to becoming a competent problem solver, and was gaining the sense of independence and emotional resilience that went along with it.

▶ **Key Take-Away**
Providing your child with opportunities to solve problems throughout the day supports the development of problem solving skills and emotional resilience.

Identify the Real Problem

When problems arise in life, it is essential to accurately identify what the problem is in order to be able to solve it. This can be difficult for some children, particularly those who are young or who have attention, anxiety, mood, and behavior challenges. They may identify that the problem lies with someone or something else, rather than being able to understand their role in the situation. A child who falls off his bike may say "that stupid rock hit my tire" and assess that the problem is the rock, rather than identifying the real problem of not watching what was in front of him such that he hit the rock rather than steering around it.

It is important for parents to understand that children may express upset about something that does not represent the underlying problem, which distracts from the real issues that require attention. Consider the child with attention and learning challenges who refuses to do an assignment in class because "it's stupid and I don't want to do it." This type of response is generally rooted in a fear of failure, fear of looking stupid or poor frustration tolerance. Some children would rather be the "naughty kid" than the "stupid kid," especially in the presence of peers.

While it may seem that the problem is the assignment or the child's poor attitude, the real underlying problems are feelings of incompetence and fear of failure. Children can go on for many years avoiding real problems because adults are focused on dealing with the surface issues of their refusal behavior or poor attitude. It is important that both adults and children be able to identify the real problem so that appropriate solutions can be developed.

Common situations in which children may inaccurately assess the real problem include:

- *A college-age child blames his poor exam grade* on the professor, believes the problem is that the exam was unfair and that the professor doesn't like him.

- *A child who has no clean socks to wear to school* thinks that the problem lies with his parents who did not wash them.

- *A young child cannot find the toy he is looking for,* and perceives that the problem is his mother's refusal to help him find it.

- *A teen who is getting in trouble for constant fighting with his sister* reports that the problem is his father putting limits on his video game usage, which causes him to be bored.

- *An older child continues to oversleep in the mornings,* and feels the problem is that her mother is not coming in to make sure she is up and getting ready.

It is important to recognize that children may genuinely perceive that the problem is one thing even though it is clear to adults that it is another. Parents need to work on expanding the child's understanding of the root problem so he can accurately identify what needs to be solved. The child who oversleeps and feels the problem is her mother not waking her and repeatedly checking on her, needs to see that the real problem may be not setting her alarm, not getting out of bed because she would prefer not to, and not keeping track of the time. The child with no clean socks needs to move to an understanding that the real problem is not putting dirty clothing in the hamper to be washed.

It is important for children to develop the cognitive skill of problem identification. They have no hope of successfully solving problems if they can't accurately determine what the problem is in the first place.

Important things to keep in mind when working with your child to better grasp the real problems that arise include:

- *Allow your child to experience problems* so he can think through them. Children who are sheltered from problems, and whose parents jump in to solve them, cannot develop awareness of what the problems are.

- *Accept your child's perception of the problem,* and guide him to consider alternatives. It is not helpful to tell the child that his analysis of the situation is "wrong," as this will only lead to defensiveness and upset. Instead, let your child know that you understand his perception and then offer some other ideas of what the problem could be.

- *Help your child make a list,* either verbally or on paper, of all possibilities for what the real problem might be. Go through them together to talk about which one might make the most sense and is likely to be the core issue.

- *Once you have identified the real problem,* you can move into the process of developing solutions.

Children who are unable to perceive the real problem are also at risk for believing that no matter what they do, they can not influence their situation or make anything better. Blaming other people, objects, or situations for their problems leads to an external locus of control, believing that other people, things, and circumstances have control over what happens to them rather than having any control or influence. This is very detrimental as it encourages children to see themselves as victims of whatever happens in their lives, and does not instill a sense of being able to influence the outcomes they experience.

It is important for children to develop the cognitive skill of problem identification. They have no hope of successfully solving problems if they can't accurately determine what the problem is in the first place. This process can be quite simple when children are young, but will naturally expand over time as the problems they encounter become larger and more complex with age. Parents need to look below the surface to assess what the real underlying problem may be, and then help the child to become aware of it so appropriate solutions can be developed.

> ▶ **Key Take-Away**
> Teaching children to accurately identify the problems they encounter is essential to helping them feel a sense of control over their lives and circumstances, and to implement effective solutions.

Identify Possible Solutions

Now that you have an understanding of how you and your child can more accurately identify specific problems that arise, your attention is now on helping your child develop appropriate solutions. When faced with a problem, your child genuinely may not be able to come up with solutions or may believe he cannot come up with one. I find that children often have some idea of what they could do to solve a problem, but their initial response is usually, "I have no idea."

When you first begin working on this skill, the list of solutions your child is able to generate on his own may be very short—or even nonexistent! It may also be the case that the ways your child tries to solve problems are inefficient or ineffective. This can happen when children do not really take time to think through their solutions, or because they lack experience. Children will generally require specific guidance and support to generate more sophisticated and efficient solutions.

There are ways to help children identify potential solutions. Some can work through solution development verbally, while others benefit from writing them down or drawing pictures to helpthem process and retain their ideas. The following options can assist with generating a list of possible solutions:

- *Have your child brainstorm* all possible solutions he can come up with as a starting point. Allow your child to generate whatever solutions come to his mind without judging the ideas he presents, as this will typically have the effect of shutting down his thinking and contributions.

- *Offer ideas* that you have for how to solve the problem.

- *Share solutions* that have worked for you in similar situations.

- *Have your child ask siblings,* extended family members, coaches, teachers or others what has worked for them.

- *Help your child reflect* on past experience to recall strategies used previously.

- *Encourage your child* to think about solutions he has seen others use.

Once your child has identified some potential solutions, it is important to think through which option to try first. This requires appraisal skills that your child may need support and instruction to develop. If needed, you will want to help your child think through the likely outcomes of each option; how long each might take; and whether he has the required materials or resources to make it work. It is important to have your child consider which options may be easier or more difficult, as children sometimes come up with options that could work but are not efficient or feasible.

This process of helping your child generate and select solutions may feel cumbersome, but it is essential for improving your child's ability to think through problems more effectively on his own.

CODY'S STORY

Cody was in fifth grade when his parents brought him to my office because of ongoing concerns about his mood and behavior issues. He was highly reactive, and would become easily upset anytime something happened that was unexpected or that he considered unpleasant. His behavior ranged from complaining and arguing to yelling and physical aggression. Though he was taking many psychiatric medications and receiving social work services at school, his issues were not improving.

After speaking with Cody and his parents, it was clear that he lacked problem-solving skills; and he was blowing up as a result of not seeing any other option when challenges arose. Cody was eating a diet high in junk foods, and his parents noted that he had persistent low energy throughout the day as a result of the sedating medications he was prescribed. I explained to them that there were multiple solutions we could implement to improve his symptoms by including a nutrition plan, neurofeedback, collaboration with his psychiatrist, parent training, and teaching problem-solving skills. They were eager to get going with all of these options, as they had become worn out from constantly trying to help their son without getting very far.

In the realm of cognitive strategies, I had his parents begin by increasing the amount of problem-solving opportunities Cody had each day. Because of his high reactivity, we needed to start with very small problems such as moving items aside in the refrigerator to find the food he was looking for, cleaning up small messes when they occurred, and helping his dad put new batteries in his remote control car. Once he was solving small problems with his parents, we began to teach the process of identifying the specific problem he encountered.

This was challenging, as he often would identify that the problem was someone else not doing something for him or not allowing him to do something he wanted to do. With his parents' guidance he began over time to more accurately identify problems when they occurred instead of just reacting to them. When we moved to the stage of generating solutions, Cody really struggled. His first inclination was to say, "I have no idea!" or "How would I know!" when a problem arose and he was asked to help generate solutions.

For a few weeks, I had his parents simply offer the opportunity for him to come up with ideas by saying, "Maybe you have an idea for how we could solve this." If he was unresponsive or said he didn't know, I asked parents to offer their own suggestions. This modeling was an important step for Cody to sense that his parents were supportive rather than demanding, and also to help him get a sense of the kinds of solutions available to him.

Over those initial weeks, Cody slowly began to come up with some ideas of his own. They weren't always effective solutions, but he was at least thinking and contributing ideas. His parents incorporated various strategies such as having him ask others for their ideas, including the PE teacher at school who had a very good rapport with Cody and whom he respected. With time and practice, Cody was better able to pause and think through the situation when he encountered problems. It certainly didn't happen overnight, but Cody's parents were consistent and persistent in their efforts to help him cope with challenges instead of merely reacting to them.

> **Key Take-Away**
> Guiding children to generate and think through potential solutions is a critical part of helping them learns to manage and solve problems independently.

Problem-Solving Journals

A simple and effective tool for teaching problem-solving skills is the problem-solving journal. It is essentially a notebook in which children keep a list of potential problems and solutions, problems they have already encountered, and the solutions that did or did not work. This same concept can be effectively used in various formats (pictures, words, or a combination of both) with children from preschool age through postsecondary.

Children should be encouraged to take ownership of their journals by choosing their container (binder, notebook, computer file, etc.) and decorating it however they like. It may also be helpful for children to name their journal, if they so desire. Children can come up with creative names, some of my favorites to date being "Dylan's Toughies," "P&A" (Problems and Answers), and "Got Problems?"

There are two main types of entries that go into these journals:

- potential problems; and
- problems that have already been experienced.

In the case of *potential problems*, you first help the child identify possible problems that could arise in a given situation. If the child is getting ready to write a paper, he will think through all the potential problems that could come up throughout the process. An example for young children could be thinking about possible problems that could arise when they make a craft, or play with their siblings outside. Once potential problems have been identified, they then start to generate potential solutions.

Most, regardless of age, will initially need some support to come up with solutions. This entire process of identifying potential problems and solutions helps build the skill of foresight, thinking about things ahead of time to better approach the situation. It also builds resilience, and improves frustration tolerance once they are engaged in that task and encounter a problem because they have already anticipated and thought through options.

After the situation has come and gone, children can review their journal entries to determine which if any of the potential problems came up, or if another unforeseen problem arose. They can also look at their list of potential solutions to determine which one(s) were most effective, and add a new solution that they may have discovered.

An example of the problem-solving journal in action is a situation in which an older elementary student was assigned to a new bus route. That new route required her to change buses at a different school before arriving at her own. This was a situation with the potential for lots of problems! We decided to use her problem-solving journal to discuss possible issues beforehand. In one column on the paper, we generated a list of the potential problems that could occur: getting on the wrong bus, not finding the right bus, missing the bus, etc.

In another column, we came up with possible solutions to these problems: look at the bus number, ask the bus driver if it is the right bus, find the line monitor to ask for help, etc. A third column was left blank for us to fill in once she had actually encountered that situation. After any such incident had happened, we referred to the journal and marked which problems had actually occurred and which solutions worked or did not work.

The process of previewing and reviewing problems in this way is very beneficial for helping children become more proficient with problem solving and flexible thinking in general. They are also able to see that sometimes we come up with ideas and plans that do not work well in the moment, requiring us to go back to the drawing board to figure out alternate solutions.

The other type of entry that could go into a problem-solving journal is for a *situation that has already been experienced*. In this case, children can list what the problem was and how they dealt with it at the time. The third column is used for marking whether or not the solutions worked, as well as adding any additional solutions that are thought of after the fact. I have had some children use a high-lighter or some kind of notation to mark the solutions they would like to try the next time they encounter the same problem.

This type of entry can be reviewed repeatedly as similar problems are encountered, in order to help children connect past and present experiences and continue to refine their ability to generate flexible and appropriate solutions.

▶ **Key Take-Away**

Problem-solving journals are a simple way to teach children to anticipate problems they may encounter, as well as to reflect on past experiences in order to learn from them.

CHAPTER 23

DEVELOPING
AWARENESS &
POSITIVE THINKING

*Teaching children to be mindful can
reduce hyperactivity, stress and anxiety.*

Mindfulness is a concept gaining more attention in recent years, so you may have heard the term. It simply means being attentive, aware, and open to what is happening in the present moment. That includes awareness of feelings, thoughts, actions, etc., without judging them or doing anything about them. There is a significant amount of research on mindfulness for adults and children, and it is recognized as a beneficial component of stress and anxiety reduction.[1] Cultivating better awareness of your own experience in the moment is key to becoming more resilient, and being able to manage uncomfortable or stressful situations that arise.

There are many ways to cultivate mindfulness in children, and parents need to select options that are appropriate based on their child's age and developmental level.

Many children with attention, anxiety, mood, and behavior challenges struggle with slowing their brains and bodies long enough to actually think about and experience what is going on in the moment. They tend to seek out stimulation constantly, and may be highly uncomfortable with not having something going on to occupy their body and/or mind every moment.

Stimulation can include physical movement such as pacing, having the television on in the background even when not watching it, absorption in video games, or repetitive self-stimulatory physical behaviors such as hand flapping. The more uncomfortable and dysregulated these children feel, the more they seek out external stimulation to distract and avoid the sensations and thoughts they are experiencing. While this may temporarily make them feel better, over the long term it leads to poor resilience and coping.

Teaching children to be mindful can reduce stress, anxiety, hyperactivity and emotional and behavioral reactivity. It is vital to the process of helping these children develop a "pause button" so they have the capacity to think before reacting. There are many ways to cultivate mindfulness in children, and parents need to select options that are appropriate based on their child's age and developmental level. Below are some options to help you get started:

- *Belly Breathing*

  Breathing is obviously something you do constantly, but generally without being aware of it. Focusing on breathing is an opportunity to slow down and become mindful of what is happening in our body. This can be done anytime or anywhere, but it is often best to start by sitting or lying down in a quiet area. The goal is to engage in "belly breathing" so that your child takes deeper breaths.

Show your child what it means to take a deep breath by placing your hand and/or their hand on your stomach and breathing so that the hand(s) rise on your belly. You can also have them lie down with a small toy or object on their belly, which they then try to move up and down as they breathe. Use counting to help pace the breathing, such as breathing in for a slow count of three and out for a count of three. If your child is capable of adding another step, have him breath in through his nose and out through his mouth while you count.

Slow paced deep breathing promotes mindful awareness of the body, as well as reduces anxiety and stress.

- *The Bell Exercise*

Have your child sit or lie down with eyes closed. Ask him to become aware of his breathing. Tell them that you will ring a bell (or chime or any other sound that is not annoying to him). Your child is to stay still and listen to the sound, raising his hand or opening his eyes when he can no longer hear the sound.

This is a very brief exercise that promotes focus on one thing (the sound of the bell) for a period of time.

- *"Do Nothing" Pose*

This is a simple children's yoga pose that entails lying on the floor and doing nothing for a period of time. It can be an excellent starting point for any child, and can be done even by children with more severe disabilities. The child can lie however he would like, but it is ideal to lie with arms and legs flat on the ground so that the entire body has contact with the floor beneath him.

Start with an amount of time that is doable for your child, which could be just 5-10 seconds, and increase from there. Continue to extend the amount of time your child can lie on the ground without doing anything.

This is a great exercise to do with your child, as every adult can benefit from periods of "doing nothing" as well!

- *Mindful Snacking*

Prepare a small snack and eat it with your child, and focus on being mindful about the process. Take small bites, chew slowly, and stay aware of how the food smells, looks, sounds, feels, and tastes. Talk about the experience of eating as you do so, and take your time with it.

- *Coloring*

The act of coloring has long promoted focus and relaxation for many children (and adults) who do not struggle with fine-motor issues. Coloring promotes calm focused attention, and hones our awareness of color, texture and visual aesthetics. There are many wonderful coloring books available even for older children and adults, including designs such as mandalas that are particularly useful for promoting mind-fulness and relaxation.

- *Squeeze and Relax*

  This can be done as a full-body activity or with specific body parts. Simply have your child sit or lie down, close his eyes, and tightly squeeze every muscle in his body for a few seconds before releasing. You can also do this with isolated body parts such as squeezing hands into fists, squeezing thighs together, or squeezing eyes tightly closed.

  The goal is to experience the shift between moments of physical tension and relaxation. It helps children tune in to physical sensation, thus promoting mindful attention and awareness.

> ### ▶ Key Take-Away
> Activities that promote mindfulness help children slow down, improve awareness, attend to what is going on within and around them, and develop the ability to think before acting.

Positive Focus

If you have a child who is persistently negative in attitude and approach, you are likely worn out from trying to put a positive spin on things. It is important to understand that all humans have a neurological negativity bias, meaning our brains are more attuned to negative information than to positive.[2] This makes it is easier for us to retain and focus on negative things that happen to us as opposed to the positive.

While this is true to some extent for everyone, some people exhibit negativity bias to an extreme and become so chronically focused on the negative that they are unable to perceive or appreciate the positive. This can be especially true for children with attention, anxiety, mood, and behavior challenges. They can more easily become stuck on negative things that have happened to them, to the point that they assume future experiences will be negative as well. They may be convinced they will never do well with something, will not enjoy certain experiences, or even that no one likes them.

Negative outlooks can be frustrating for parents, and arguments can ensue when adults attempt to get children to take a more positive outlook on things.

When parents analyze their communication with their child who exhibits emotional and behavioral challenges, they may be surprised to find how heavily weighted toward the negative it tends to be.

Research on negativity bias has also shed light on how to more effectively use communication to overcome one's negative tendencies.[3] It turns out that the ideal ratio of positive to negative comments in communication with family members or coworkers is around 5-6 positive comments for every one negative comment. Likewise, more positive people are able to think three positive thoughts for every one negative thought. This is helpful information, as it allows you to shift your communication and focus to more effectively help children see and internalize positives rather than solely focusing on negatives.

When parents analyze their communication with their child who exhibits emotional and behavioral challenges, they are often surprised to find how heavily weighted toward the negative it tends to be. This can easily happen when adults need to spend a significant amount of time redirecting inappropriate behavior, pointing out the things that need to improve, or implementing consequences.

Children with attention, anxiety, mood, and behavior challenges can spend a significant amount of time at home and school hearing negative feedback. In order to help them shift to a more positive focus, you need to be intentional about providing a much higher ratio of positive to negative comments over the course of the day.

Here are some simple ways to help your child maintain a more positive outlook:

- *During family dinners,* take time to go around the table so each person can share one positive thing that happened to him or her that day. It could be something that turned out better than the person thought it would, or something that made him or her feel good.

- *Point out the positive things* you see your child doing throughout the day. Remember that the negative things they do are more likely to stand out, so be intentional about seeing all the positive things that your child says and does.

- *Be aware of your own bias toward negativity.* Strive to model for your children positive thoughts and focus in your own life and circumstances. Children who constantly hear their parents express a "glass half empty" attitude toward life will tend to adopt the same thought process.

- *Focusing on gratitude* promotes positive thoughts, emotions and actions. Build a family habit of expressing thanks for things daily, or include a gratitude element in the bedtime routine by sharing something you are each grateful for that day.

- *When your child expresses negativity about himself or a task,* be intentional about acknowledging how he feels while also offering a more positive way of thinking about it. For example, your child may say something like, "This is way too much work. I'm never going to figure it out!" while working on homework. You could respond with, "I know it feels really tough, but I also know that you've figured out tough things before because you are a hard worker."

    It is essential to acknowledge the negative emotion the child is experiencing, before offering a positive alternative. This allows your child to know he has been heard, and helps avoid defensiveness or arguments.

- *If you are heading into a situation or task* with your child that tends to be challenging or upsetting, try previewing the experience with positive self-talk. Before the event or task begins, you can help your child think about positive things that could happen; and then rehearse positive self-talk such as, "I know this will be difficult, but I can do it!"

- *Whenever you need to give your child constructive criticism or feedback* about something negative that occurred, try opening with a positive first. In the case of a child who left a red sock in the white load of wash, it would be appropriate to address it by saying something like, "I know you worked really hard on getting your laundry sorted, and I appreciate you helping out with that. Next time, please go through and double check your pile of whites to make sure you don't have any red socks hiding in there."

By opening with a positive comment, you prime the child's brain to focus on positive thoughts in order to be more receptive to the negative thought that follows it. When you begin a comment or discussion with the negative, it often has the effect of your child not even hearing any positive comments that may follow.

- *Have your child keep a journal or folder of positive things* that happen so he can refer to it when he becomes consumed with negative thoughts about himself or his experiences. He can keep notes on positive things that happen, papers with good grades or positive comments from teachers, awards they receive, and anything else that marks a positive moment in their life. Looking back through these things on challenging days can help shift to a more positive outlook.

If your child has a chronically negative outlook, being intentional about spotlighting positives throughout the day can help balance out his negative thoughts and emotions. Your goal is not to try to get your child to agree with your positive viewpoint, or to convince him to be more positive. Rather, you want to infuse more positive thoughts and feelings throughout the day to provide a model for more positive thinking.

Helping your child focus on positive behaviors, experiences and feelings will help him more effectively weather challenges that come his way without becoming absorbed in negativity.

> ### ▶ Key Take-Away
>
> Spotlighting positive experiences, modeling our own positive outlook, and communicating in more positive ways can help children with chronically negative attitudes shift toward a more positive focus.

part seven: **supporting parent and family needs**

CHAPTER 24

PARENT NEEDS

Children can only be as emotionally and
behaviorally regulated as their parents.

After providing you with various solutions to address your child's challenges, I would be remiss if I did not give some information regarding parent needs and potential obstacles to implementing these strategies. The focus of this book is obviously on helping your child, but the personal and relational struggles going on in a parent's life impact the ability to make progress with children. My twenty years of working with families has taught me that parents need support and strategies to address their own challenges so they can best implement the tools needed for their children to improve.

While we have yet to fully understand how and why an increasing number of children develop attention, anxiety, mood, and behavior challenges, we do know that there is a complex interplay of many factors—including genetics and environmental factors.[1]

With the exception of situations involving significant parental abuse or neglect, parents are **not** the cause of their child's symptoms and challenges. As a parent of a child with these challenges, it is important to understand that you are not to blame for your child's difficulties. You did not cause your child to have problems with attention, anxiety, mood or behavior, but you have the power to improve your child's situation moving forward. As a parent, you have the most important relationship with your child; you are the primary and trusted guide on the journey of development. The way that you interact and model your own thoughts and emotions play a significant role in how your child learns to think, feel and behave.

It is important to remember that in general, children can only be as emotionally and behaviorally regulated as their parents.

Parents' issues and functioning impact the child in various ways. Those who are highly anxious, highly reactive, or who have chronically high stress levels often struggle to consistently implement the types of solutions needed for child symptom improvement. Research has shown that stress is also "contagious," meaning that parents who experience chronic stress can influence their children to develop chronic levels of stress.[2] This relates to the concept of bi-directional relationships between parents and children, as it means that parents influence children just as children influence parents.

There is a constant back-and-forth emotional and behavioral interaction between parents and children that helps shape both the child and the parents.[3] This helps explain why children are so readily influenced by the emotional states of parents. Even young children can sense the emotional state of a parent and be impacted by it.

When a parent is chronically reactive, for example, this can be dysregulating to the child and cause the child to develop more emotional reactivity. Parents with high anxiety can pass anxiety on to children simply by the ways their own thoughts, emotions and behaviors are modeled for the child. Children pick up on emotions and behaviors between adults as well, and can be significantly impacted by tension, fighting, and poor communication between parents. As parents, you do not intend to pass on these issues to your children or negatively impact them with your personal and relational problems, but it happens without realizing it.

It is important to remember that in general, children can only be as emotionally and behaviorally regulated as their parents. A parent who is consistently fearful, angry, avoidant, explosive, or impulsive may see these same characteristics crop up in their children. It is difficult to guide a child to stay calm, resist impulsive actions, and worry less when a parent is consistently reactive, impulsive and anxious. If you want to help your children be more emotionally and behaviorally regulated, then you have to be willing to acknowledge your own issues and work toward addressing them.

Take Time for Yourself

It is common for parents, especially mothers, to focus solely on their child's needs and ignore their own. Taking time to rest, relax and rejuvenate is essential for effective parenting. Many parents feel they are unable to prioritize their own care and needs due to lack of time, energy, money, or support. While there can certainly be logistical issues to resolve, planning for time away from the constant demands of children and everyday life is essential.

Parents who do not spend any time meeting their own needs are prone to emotional and physical burnout. Just as you must consider your child's need for downtime, as parents you also require adequate amounts of downtime to avoid exhaustion and resentment. Whether it is a bath, sitting at a coffee shop to read, watching a movie, taking a nap, or whatever else is relaxing and rejuvenating to you, take at least a little time each week to do something you like without your child(ren).

> Parenting a child with special needs is a marathon—not a sprint. Taking care of yourself will help you have the health, energy and emotional resources to be the parent your child needs now and in the future.

While it may seem challenging to take time for yourself, there are always options. You may have a spouse, family member, friend, or babysitter who can spend time with your child while you take time for yourself. If this is not possible, then take some time for yourself while your child is sleeping or at school. I have yet to work with parents who could not find some amount of time, however brief, to do something for themselves on a daily or weekly basis. Time away from your children to do something for yourselves is essential to maintaining your ability to effectively parent. Parenting a child with special needs is a marathon—not a sprint. Taking care of yourself will help you have the health, energy and emotional resources to be the parent your child needs now and in the future.

Manage Your Own Anxiety

Having a child who tends to be resistive, reactive and unpredictable can raise any parent's anxiety level. When parenting a child with challenges, it is easy to get swept up in a host of anxieties about the child's functioning both now and in the future, as well as what this means for the family as a whole. As parent anxieties increase, so do the child's. This can lead to a chronic pattern of anxiety in the family, which negatively impacts everyone's functioning.

It is helpful for parents to focus on staying in the "here and now" in order to resist getting caught up in anxious thoughts about what the future may hold. If your child is having a meltdown, your mind may immediately fast-forward many years into the future with thoughts of "what if my child is still doing this at age 20?!" Allowing your mind to engage in future time travel is unhelpful in the present moment, as it simply fuels anxiety and distress, making it more difficult to think about and appropriately manage what is going on right now. Try to stay calm and focus on what is happening in the moment, as this will keep you out of fight-or-flight mode, and allow you to appropriately respond to whatever is happening with your child.

If you find yourself getting caught up in anxiety, try stepping away from the situation to give yourself a little break. Sometimes "time out" can be as necessary for adults as it is for children! Allow yourself to step away for a few minutes to reset your thoughts and emotions, and then come back to handle whatever happened with your child. When you recognizing your own anxiety level, and then find ways to effectively reduce it, is essential for supporting your child's growth and development—especially during challenging moments.

Acknowledge & Address Personal Issues

Just as children can have issues, challenges and symptoms, so can parents. You are human and have specific strengths and weaknesses unique to you. Some parents may have their own diagnoses of physical and/or mental health; others may experience symptoms that have never been diagnosed. Research says that parents of children with special needs tend to have higher levels of depression and anxiety than other parents.[4] It makes sense that this would be the case, as parenting children with challenges can stretch mental, emotional and tangible resources.

Some children have such extensive needs that parents are forced to leave their jobs, drain finances, and change many other aspects of their lives in order to care for their child. It can be frustrating, anxiety provoking and discouraging to have a child who is resistive, reactive and responds in unpredictable ways. Many parents feel as if they are walking on eggshells with their children day and night, and that can quickly become exhausting and demoralizing.

Children don't come with instruction manuals—especially children with attention, anxiety, mood, and behavior challenges.

Adding children into the mix of one's life brings an entirely new set of responsibilities and emotions, and this can be an especially difficult adjustment when the child has developmental or mental health needs. You may feel ill equipped to manage the needs of your child, and this is not unusual. Children don't come with instruction manuals—especially children with attention, anxiety, mood, and behavior challenges. I have had refreshingly honest parents state that "this isn't what we thought we were signing on for when we decided to have children!"

There are many completely normal emotions parents experience when they realize their child has challenges, including sadness, grief, worry, anger, and guilt. Some parents are able to recognize and manage these emotions more effectively than others. If you were already struggling with your own emotions and behavior prior to having a child, these additional negative emotions may be especially difficult for you to work through. When parents become stuck in a mode of chronic negative emotion as a result of their experience with their child, it is appropriate to seek help to process and move past those negative thoughts and emotions.

> Be willing to get help for the
> issues you are facing.

I encourage all parents to be honest with themselves about their own issues, and to seek help and support to better address them. It does not benefit you or your child to pretend your own difficulties with attention, anxiety, mood, and behavior do not exist. In fact, ignoring the role your personal challenges play in your ability to parent will only lead to increased distress and difficulty with your child. Be willing to get help for the issues you are facing. Some of the supports and treatments parents at my clinic find most helpful include counseling, diet changes and nutritional supplementation, neurofeedback, sleep supports, and mindfulness training.

The philosophy upon which I have based my clinic is that parents need support just as much as children do. It does no good to focus all the attention on children in treatment without addressing the needs of their parents. That is why we involve parents with their children in almost every aspect of treatment, and provide support and intervention specifically to parents as well. The healthier and happier parents are, the more we can help them accomplish with their children.

I encourage all parents to be honest with themselves about their own issues, and to seek help and support to better address them. It does not benefit you or your child to pretend your own difficulties with attention, anxiety, mood, and behavior do not exist.

CHAPTER 25

FAMILY NEEDS

*When parents see their child's issues
very differently, it can be difficult or impossible
to develop consistent approaches to address
the child's needs.*

While the challenges of raising a child with developmental and mental health needs can take a toll on parents as individuals, they can also take a roll on relationships. Even the strongest marriages and co-parenting relationships can become strained under the realities of raising children with these kinds of concerns. Just as it is important to acknowledge and address personal issues you may have, it is also necessary to be honest about the state of your relationship with your significant other or co-parent.

In my work with patients and their families, it is not unusual to have situations where the child's needs are being used as a way to avoid or ignore very real problems in the marriage or co-parenting relationship. Parents who are not on the same page with regard to their parenting, may have different opinions on the needs of the child. If they are also experiencing struggles in their relationship with one another, they will have a more difficult time implementing the strategies necessary for improving their child's symptoms.

When parents see their child's issues very differently, it can be difficult or impossible to develop consistent approaches to address the child's needs. Sometimes one parent believes there are significant problems that need to be addressed, while the other parent denies that any issues exist. One parent may be more likely to enforce rules and expectations, while the other is permissive and does anything possible to avoid conflict. In such situations, it is typically necessary to work with a professional who can facilitate discussion and compromise about how to best move forward with the child.

Parents bring their own strengths and challenges to the parenting process, and ideally the goal should be to complement each other so the child benefits from the best each has to offer. This can be difficult to manage without a third party facilitating healthy communication, and I encourage you to seek out support in this area if this is an issue you are facing.

Child sleep problems are particularly problematic for relationships between parents. When a child does not sleep independently, it can cause breakdowns in relationships because one or both parents are consumed with trying to get the child to fall and stay asleep throughout the night. This infringes on the time parents have to spend together while children are sleeping, and can take a significant toll on the marriage relationship.

I have worked with some parents who have not slept together in the same bed for many years because of their child's sleep issues. This can lead to an unhealthy spousal relationship on many levels. It can also be the case that parents are unwilling to work on helping their child learn to sleep in their own bed because of the discomfort they have toward their spouse. Having the child in bed with them provides a buffer, allowing them to avoid dealing with the reality of spending time alone, or being intimate with their significant other.

Dysfunctional cycles like this can develop and persist between parents for a variety of reasons, and these patterns of interaction and behavior require specific attention in order to support the health of the relationship—let alone the well-being of the child. Again, if this is an issue between you and your significant other, accessing professional support to work through this issue will benefit you and your child.

> Each parent is responsible for his or her own attitudes and actions regarding the child, and one cannot control the other. Attempts to micro-manage or control the other parent leads to increasing resentment, frustration and tension.

Sometimes it is the case that two parents cannot or will not work toward resolving their relationship issues. One parent may want to work on them, while the other is avoidant or resistive. It is then necessary to let go of things you cannot control, and focus on what you can control. Each parent is responsible for his or her own attitudes and actions regarding the child, and one cannot control the other. Attempts to micro-manage or control the other parent leads to increasing resentment, frustration and tension. If this is the reality in your relationship, I encourage you to work on letting go of what you cannot control. Some can do this on their own, while others require professional support to release unhelpful thoughts, feelings and behaviors related to the other parent. Focus on your own interactions and implementation of strategies with your child, knowing he is better off for the efforts you make even if the other parent is not doing the same.

> Just as it is important to take time for yourself as an individual, it is also important to prioritize time together as a couple.

If you are in a relationship with a spouse or significant other, it is important to prioritize that relationship and spend time strengthening it. Children benefit most when their parents have a strong relationship with one another. Just as it is important to take time for yourself as an individual, it is also important to prioritize time together as a couple. This may mean making time to go out for coffee or a meal periodically, watch a favorite television show together, or something as mundane as grocery shopping together without the kids. Spending time as a couple without the children does not have to require extensive time or money. Consistently connecting in meaningful ways, however brief, will benefit you, your relationship, and your children.

Sibling & Extended Family Issues

There can be specific challenges in families where the child with attention, anxiety, mood, and behavior issues has siblings. Children with these kinds of needs often require more time and attention from parents than the others. Jealousy, resentment and frustration for siblings may be the outcome; these emotional responses are to be expected. It can be difficult for parents to balance the needs of all their children, and to help children understand the needs of their sibling with special needs. Open communication is certainly critical in these situations, as it is important to acknowledge sibling feelings.

Too often parents avoid talking about how their other children feel in relation to a sibling with special needs, and this is a mistake. All children in the family need the opportunity to openly express how they feel, and to know that it is normal for them to have some negative emotions about the situation. Parents should provide information about the child's needs and challenges at a level the siblings can comprehend. It is also important to communicate that siblings are not to blame for these challenges, nor are they responsible for making them better.

An excellent source of information and support related to the needs of siblings is The Sibling Support Project. This organization has created what I believe is the most effective model for addressing the needs of siblings of children with special needs. Their renowned Sibshop groups and events allow siblings to connect, learn, and have fun with other siblings who understand their situation. Our clinic runs Sibshop groups throughout the year as do many other clinics and organizations around the world. Locating a group in your area may be a very helpful way to meet the needs of the other children in your family.

Another family issue that can come up is in relation to extended family members. Grandparents and extended family members can be a support to parents of children with developmental and mental health challenges, but there can also be difficulties that arise. While most grandparents and other family members aim to be helpful, they may not understand the reality of your child's situation; and they may struggle to know how best to help. Providing family members with information about your child's needs and the strategies you use to support them is important.

If conflicts or issues arise in relation to your approach with your child, open communication is generally needed to resolve them. Extended family members can be a valuable source of support both emotionally and tangibly. If difficulties arise with grandparents or other family members, try to resolve them rather than avoiding them. While it is not always possible to gain appropriate support and understanding from extended family members, I find that providing clear information and strategies goes a long way toward making these relationships workable.

Seek Out Support & Assistance When Needed

I do not believe any parent can fully support their child's needs alone, regardless of whether the child has challenges or not. We all benefit from support and assistance from others, be they family members, friends, school professionals, therapy providers, church members, community groups, or other individuals or organizations in our lives. The African proverb "it takes a village to raise a child" is very true, and perhaps even more so in the case of children with attention, anxiety, mood, and behavior challenges. The experience of raising a child with these needs can feel isolating and lonely as friends, coworkers, and even family members may struggle to understand the realities of your situation. Many of the parents I work with have had their friendships or group involvement fall by the wayside because the majority of their time is spent supporting their child, or because they no longer have as many things in common and feel misunderstood.

> The African proverb "it takes a village to raise a child" is very true, and perhaps even more so in the case of children with attention, anxiety, mood, and behavior challenges.

While there is the potential to feel isolated and as if no one wants to help, it does not have to be that way. If your current group of friends or organizations in which you have been involved are no longer a good fit for your current life circumstances, then it is necessary to find new ways to connect with others and get support. For some parents, this means participating in support groups for parents of children with challenges. Others find that involvement in community activities for individuals and families with special needs connects them to people who understand and can provide valuable emotional support.

Over the years, I have seen more churches and community organizations recognizing the needs of parents and families of children with developmental and mental health needs, and responding with opportunities for them. If the churches or other organizations in your life do not yet have support options set up for families such as yours, talk to their leaders about your needs. Do not assume that no one is interested in supporting you or your child. It is likely that they are unaware of your needs or how to best support them, but would be receptive to learning and developing solutions. When I have encouraged parents to reach out and ask for what they need, the response in most cases has been very positive for everyone involved.

Do not assume that no one is interested in supporting you or your child. It is likely that they are unaware of your needs or how to best support them.

Do not fall into the trap of believing that you can be everything and do everything for your child. Accept that you need support and assistance, at least some of the time; ask for help when needed. Remember, you are in a marathon to support your child's development; you need the support of a village to avoid burnout.

CHAPTER 26

FINAL WORDS

Even in the midst of the toughest and most demanding phases of life with a child, there are positives.

As parents, you have goals and ambitions for your children as you constantly strive to help them improve. When a child has attention, anxiety, mood and behavior challenges, there tends to be a constant drive to work on these issues and to look for things that could be improved. You may sometimes feel that no matter how hard you try, your child will never improve; or that there are always going to be more problems and skills to tackle. This can lead to a situation where you are unable to recognize or celebrate successes that occur with your child.

Celebrate Successes

It is critical to recognize the improvements that have already been made, and celebrate successes as they arise. Some of us have a tendency to move right to the next thing once we've accomplished something, without pausing to recognize and celebrate the current success or victory. I have worked with many parents who, when I point out a recent success for their child, respond with "Yes, but they still aren't doing x, y or z."

Failure to acknowledge improvements and successes, no matter how small, can lead to persistent frustration and a sense of "We're not getting anywhere." This is demoralizing for both the parent and the child. Being mindful of the positive changes you and your child are making, and acknowledging successes, provides motivation to continue putting forth the effort for continued change and improvement. If you don't spotlight your child's efforts and progress, it can lead to discouragement, sending the message that nothing he does is good enough. Not acknowledging the progress you are making with your parenting efforts can also increase distress and anxiety, and lead to a sense of hopelessness that anything can change for the better.

You may sometimes feel that no matter how hard you try, your child will never improve; or that there are always going to be more problems and skills to tackle. If you do, you will be unable to recognize or celebrate successes that occur with your child.

Even in midst of the toughest and most demanding phases of life with a child, there are positives that can be found. Some parents find it helpful to keep a list or journal of the successes and positive changes that occur, as these can be especially helpful to review on the inevitable days when you feel like nothing is going well. In the marathon of life with your child, take time to celebrate the small milestones along the way. You are looking for progress, not perfection. It is the accumulation of small changes in your child over time that propels you forward.

While there will always be challenges, each of us is capable of being better tomorrow than we were today. It is my hope that you now have some additional knowledge and tools to support your child and yourself on this journey.

You are by far the most important resource your child has. Take care of yourself, reach out for support as needed, and celebrate the many successes along the path of creating a better life for you, your child, and your family.

ENDNOTES

Chapter 2

1 Sarris, J., Logan, A.C., Akbaraly, T.N., Amminger, G.P., Balanza-Martinez, V., Freeman, M.P...& Jacka, F.N. (2015). Nutritional medicine as mainstream in psychiatry. *The Lancet Psychiatry, 2*(3), 271-274.

2 Kaplan, B.J., Rucklidge, J.J., Romijn, A., & McLeod, K. (2015). The emerging field of nutritional mental health: Inflammation, the microbiome, oxidative stress, and mitochondrial function. *Clinical Psychological Science, 3*(6), 964-980.

3 Foster, J.A. & Neufeld, K.A.M. (2013). Gut-brain axis: How the microbiome influences anxiety and depression. *Trends in Neuroscience, 36*(5), 305-312.

Chapter 3

1 Johnson, R.J., Gold, M.S., Johnson, D.R., Ishimoto, T., Lanaspa, M.A., Zahniser, N.R., & Avena, N.M. (2011). Attention-deficit/hyperactivity disorder: Is it time to reappraise the role of sugar consumption? *Postgraduate Medicine, 123*(5), 39-49.

2 Jones, T.W., Borg, W.P., Boulware, S.D., McCarthy, G., Sherwin, R.S., & Tamborlane, W.V. (1995). Enhanced adrenomedullar response and increased susceptibility to neuroglycopenia: Mechanisms underlying the adverse effects of sugar ingestion in healthy children. *The Journal of Pediatrics, 126*(2), 171-177.

3 Fowler, S.P., Williams, K., Resendez, R.G., Hunt, K.J., Hazuda, H.P., & Stern, M.P. (2008). Fueling the obesity epidemic? Artificially sweetened beverage use and long-term weight gain. *Obesity, 16*, 1894-1900.

4 Nweze, C.C., Mustapha, A.A., & Olose, M. (2015). Aspartame food additive and its biochemical implication: A review. *Food Science and Quality Management, 36.* Retrieved from *http://www.iiste.org/Journals/index.php/FSQM/article/view/19774*

5 Walton, R.G., Hudak, R., & Green-Waite, R.J. (1993). Adverse reactions to aspartame: Double-blind challenge in patients from a vulnerable population. *Biological Psychiatry, 34*(1-2), 13-17.

Chapter 4

1 Stevens, L.J., Burgess, J.R., Stochelski, M.A., & Kuczek, T. (2015). Amounts of artificial food dyes and added sugars in foods and sweets commonly consumed by children. *Clinical Pediatrics, 54*(4), 309-321.

2 Gaby, A.R. (1998). The role of hidden food allergy/intolerance in chronic disease. *Alternative Medicine Review, 3*(2), 90-100.

3 FASEB (1995) Analysis of Adverse Reactions to Monosodium Glutamate (MSG), Report. *Life Sciences Research Office, Federation of American Societies for Experimental Biology.* Washington, DC.

4 Stevens, L.J., Burgess, J.R., Stochelski, M.A., & Kuczek, T. (2015). Amounts of artificial food dyes and added sugars in foods and sweets commonly consumed by children. *Clinical Pediatrics, 54*(4), 309-321.

5 de Theije, C.G., Bavelaar, B.M., da Silva, S.L., Korte, S.M., Olivier, B., Garssen, J., & Kraneveld, A.D. (2014). Food allergy and food-based therapies in neurodevelopmental disorders. *Pediatric Allergy and Immunology, 25*(3), 218-226.

Chapter 5

1 Rampersaud, G.C., Pereira, M.A., Girard, B.L., Adams, J., Metzl, J.D. (2005). Breakfast habits, nutritional status, body weight, and academic performance in children and adolescents. *Journal of the American Dietetic Association, 105*(5), 742-760.

2 Benton, D., Maconie, A., & Williams, C. (2007). The influence of the glycaemic load of breakfast on the behaviour of children in school. *Physiology & Behavior, 92*(4), 717-724.

3 Liu, J., Zhao, S.R., & Reyes, T. (2015). Neurological and epigenetic implications of nutritional deficiencies on psychopathology: Conceptualization and review of evidence. *International Journal of Molecular Sciences, 16*(8), 18129-18148.

4 Gordon, H.A., Rucklidge, J.J., Blampied, N.M. & Johnstone, J.M. (2015). Clinically significant symptom reduction in children with attention-deficit/ hyperactivity disorder treated with micronutrients: An open-label reversal design study. *Journal of Child and Adolescent Psychopharmacology, 25*(10), 783-798.

5 Edmonds, C.J. & Burford, D. (2009). Should children drink more water?: The effects of drinking water on cognition in children. *Appetite, 52*(3), 776-779.

6 Benton, D. (2011). Dehydration influences mood and cognition: A plausible hypothesis? *Nutrients, 3*(5), 555-573. Popkin, B.M., D'anci, K.E., Rosenberg, I.H. (2010). Water, hydration and health. *Nutrition Reviews, 68*(8), 439-458.

Chapter 6
1 Richardson, A.J. (2003). The importance of omega-3 fatty acids for behaviour, cognition, and mood. *Scandinavian Journal of Nutrition, 47*(2), 92-98.

2 Richardson, A.J. (2006). Omega-3 fatty acids in ADHD and related neuro-developmental disorders. *International Review of Psychiatry, 18*(2), 155-172.

3 Simopoulos, A.P. (2002). The importance of the ratio of omega-6/omega-3 essential fatty acids. *Biomedicine & Pharmacotherapy, 56*(8), 365-379.

4 Bloch, M.H. & Qawasmi, A. (2011). Omega-3 fatty acid supplementation for the treatment of children with attention-deficit/hyperactivity disorder symptomology: Systematic review and meta-analysis. *Journal of the American Academy of Children & Adolescent Psychiatry, 50*(1), 991-1000.

5 Nyaradi, A., Li, J., Hickling, S., Foster, J., & Oddy, W.H. (2013). The role of nutrition in children's neurocognitive development, from pregnancy through childhood. *Frontiers in Human Neuroscience, 7*(97). Retrieved from *http://journal.frontiersin.org/article/10.3389/fnhum.2013.00097/full*

Chapter 8
1 Dement, W.C. & Mitler, M.M. (1993). It's time to wake up to the importance of sleep disorders. *Journal of the American Medical Association, 269*(12), 1548-1550.

2 Dement, W.C. & Mitler, M.M. (1993). It's time to wake up to the importance of sleep disorders. *Journal of the American Medical Association, 269*(12), 1548-1550.

3 Benca, R.M. (2005). Diagnosis and treatment of chronic insomnia: A review. *Psychiatric Services, 56*(3), 332-343.

4 Hirshkowitz, M., Whiton, K., Albert, S.M., Alessi, C., Bruni, O., DonCarlos, L...Hillard, P.J. (2015). National Sleep Foundation's sleep time duration recommendations: Methodology and results summary. *Sleep Health, 1*(1), 40-43.

Chapter 9

1 Mindell, J.A., Li, A.M., Sadeh, A., Kwon, R., & Goh, D.Y.T. (2015). Bedtime routines for young children: A dose-dependent association with sleep outcomes. *SLEEP, 38*(5), 717-722.

2 Hale, L. & Guan, S. (2015). Screen time and sleep among school-aged children and adolescents: A systematic literature review. *Sleep Medicine Reviews, 21*, 50-58.

3 Change, A.M., Aeschbach, D., Duffy, J.F., & Czeisler, C.A. (2014). Evening use of light- emitting eReaders negatively affects sleep, circadian timing, and next-morning alertness. *Proceedings of the National Academy of Sciences of the United States of America, 112*(4), 1232-1237.

Chapter 10

1 Lack, L.C., Gradisar, M., VanSomeren, E.J., Wright, H.R., Lushington, K. (2008). The relationship between insomnia and body temperatures. *Sleep Medicine Reviews, 12*(4), 307-317.

2 Hume, K.I. (2011). Noise pollution: A ubiquitous unrecognized disruptor of sleep? *Sleep, 34*(1), 11-23.

3 Goel, N., Kim, H., & Lao, R.P. (2005). An olfactory stimulus modifies nighttime sleep in young men and women. *Chronobiology International, 22*(5), 889-904.

4 Hoebert, M., van der Heijden, K.B., van Geijlswijk, I.M., Smits, M.G. (2009). Long-term follow-up of melatonin treatment in children with ADHD and chronic sleep onset insomnia. *Journal of Pineal Research, 47*, 1-7.

5 Gromball, J., Beschorner, F., Wantzen, C., Paulsen, U., & Burkart, M. (2014). Hyperactivity, concentration difficulties, and impulsiveness improve during seven weeks' treatment with valerian root and lemon balm extracts in primary school children. *Phytomedicine, 21*(8-9), 1098-1103

Chapter 11

1 Penedo, F.J. & Dahn, J.R. (2005). Exercise and well-being: A review of mental and physical health benefits associated with physical exercise. *Current Opinion in Psychiatry, 18*(2), 189-193.

2 Eaton, W.O., McKeen, N.A., & Campbell, D.W. (2001). The waxing and waning of movement: Implications for psychological development. *Developmental Review, 21*(2), 205-223.

3 Fakhouri, T.H.I., Hughes, J.P., Brody, D.J., Kit, B.K., Ogden, C.L. (2013). Physical activity and screen-time viewing among elementary school-aged children in the United States from 2009-2010. *JAMA Pediatrics, 167*(3), 223-229.

4 Sigman, A. (2012). Time for a view on screen time. *Archives of Disease in Childhood, 97*(11), 935-942.

5 American Academy of Pediatrics, Committee on Public Education. (2001). Children, adolescents, and television. *Pediatrics, 107*, 423-426.

6 Richards, R., McGee, R., Williams, S.M., Welch, D., & Hancox, R.J. (2010). Adolescent screen time and attachment to parents and peers. *Archives of Pediatrics & Adolescent Medicine, 164*(3), 258-262.

Chapter 13

1 Konicarova, J. & Bob, P. (2013). Principle of dissolution and primitive reflexes in ADHD. *Activitas Nervosa Superior, 55*(1-2), 74-78.

2 Bjorklund, D.F. & Brown, R.D. (1998). Physical play and cognitive development: Integrating activity, cognition, and education. *Child Development, 69*(3), 604-606.

3 Sarver, D.E., Rapport, M.D., Kofler, M.J., Raiker, J.S., & Friedman, L.M. (2015). Hyperactivity in attention-deficit/hyperactivity disorder (ADHD): Impairing deficit or compensatory behavior? *Journal of Abnormal Child Psychology, 43*(7), 1219-1232.

Chapter 14

1 Rogoff, B. (1990). *Apprenticeship in thinking: Cognitive development in social context.* New York: NY: Oxford University Press.

2 Vygotsky, L.S. (1978). *Mind in society: The development of higher psychological processes.* Cambridge, MA: Harvard University Press.

Chapter 16

1 American Psychiatric Association. (2013). Neurodevelopmental Disorders. In *Diagnostic and statistical manual of mental disorders (5th ed.).* doi:10.1176/appi.books.9780890425596.dsm01

Chapter 23

1 Mindfulness-based approaches with children and adolescents:
   A preliminary review of current research in an emergent field.
   Journal of Child and Family Studies, 19(2), 133-144.

2 Ito, T.A., Larsen, J.T., Smith, N.K., Cacioppo, J.T. (1998). Negative
   information weighs more heavily on the brain: The negativity bias in
   evaluative categorizations. *Journal of Personality and Social Psychology,
   75*(4), 887-900.

3 Losada, M. & Heaphy, E. (2004). The role of positivity and connectivity in
   the performance of business teams: A nonlinear dynamics model. *American
   Behavioral Scientist, 47*(6), 740-765.

Chapter 24

1 Tsuang, M.T., Bar, J.L., Stone, W.S., & Faraone, S.V. (2004). Gene-
   environment interactions in mental disorders. *World Psychiatry, 3*(2), 73-83.

2 Engert, V., Plessow, F., Miller, R., Kirschbaum, C., & Singer, T. (2014).
   Cortisol increase in empathic stress is modulated by emotional closeness
   and observation modality. *Psychoneuroendocrinology, 45*, 192-201.

3 Loulis, S. & Kuczynski, L. (1997). Beyond one hand clapping: Seeing
   Bidirectionality in parent-child relations. *Journal of Social and Personal
   Relationships, 14*(4), 441-461.

4 Chambers, H.G. & Chambers, J.A. (2015). Effects of caregiving on the
   families of children and adults with disabilities. *Physical Medicine and
   Rehabilitation Clinics of North America, 26*(1), 1-19.

ACKNOWLEDGMENTS

All significant accomplishments require the support of others, and writing a book is no exception. I have benefitted from the encouragement and efforts of many people who have helped make this book a reality.

I am incredibly blessed to work with amazing patients and families at my clinic each day. Thanks to all of my past and current clients for allowing me to learn from you and with you. Each of you inspires me to learn more, and to continue spreading the message that life will get better.

While owning a clinic brings both joys and challenges, by far one of the greatest benefits is getting to choose the colleagues I work with each day. A big thank you goes to my staff at Horizons who share an ongoing commitment to our mission of supporting children and families. I couldn't ask for a better group of people to work with each day.

Turning a manuscript into a book is no easy task, and I would like to thank Judith Briles and her team for creating a final product I can be proud of. The interior and exterior of this book are beautiful thanks to the design efforts of Rebecca Finkel and Ryan Jones. I would also like to thank John Rottenberg for his continued editorial support.

Much gratitude goes to JJ Virgin for giving me the push I needed to finally get this book written. I would also like to thank my Mindshare family for their constant support and encouragement. It is a privilege to be in the company of such an amazing group of professionals doing life-changing work in the world.

I have been blessed to accomplish many things thus far in my life. However, my greatest accomplishment and role by far is being the mother of four amazing children. Thank you Caden, Jonah, Nate, and Caris for your patience with me as I spent many nights and weekends writing. You are my inspiration, and I love and appreciate each one of you for who you are and who you are becoming.

Finally, there aren't adequate words to say thank you to my husband Bill, without whom this book would not have been written. Thank you for being the best at taking care of our kids and me. Everything I accomplish in my professional life is possible because of you.

WORK WITH
MY CLINIC

I founded Horizons Developmental Resource Center to meet the needs of families and individuals interested in something more than just "treatment as usual." My passion is helping children, young adults, and families get to the root of the challenges they are experiencing so they can functional optimally and achieve their fullest potential.

The multidisciplinary team of professionals at my clinic works with families and individuals throughout the United States and around the world. Whether you are looking for a one-time consultation or ongoing support, we are able to provide consultation in person as well as online.

If you are interested in what my team and I may be able to do for you and your family, please contact us to schedule a free initial phone consultation. During this 15-minute phone conversation, we will gain an understanding of your needs and share how we can best support you. To schedule this complimentary consultation, send an email to *info@horizonsdrc.com* or call (616) 698-0306.

For more information about my clinic, please visit our website at *www. HorizonsDRC.com.*

ABOUT THE AUTHOR

Nicole Beurkens, PhD is a best-selling author, award-winning therapist and speaker. A unique combination of nutritionist, special educator, and clinical psychologist, Dr. Beurkens has 20 years of experience supporting children, young adults, and families. She is an expert in evaluating and treating a wide range of learning, mood and behavior challenges, and is the founder and director of the Horizons Developmental Resource Center in Caledonia, MI.

Dr. Beurkens has developed training and educational materials for families and professionals, and speaks at events and seminars around the world. You can find her online at *www.DrBeurkens.com* where she publishes an award-winning newsletter for thousands of subscribers, and has articles and other resources available.

WWW.DRBEURKENS.COM

BONUS RESOURCES JUST FOR READERS

Go to *www.DrBeurkens.com/LifeWillGetBetterBonus* to get exclusive FREE resource downloads available only to *Life Will Get Better* readers:

- Full-color summary handouts for each section of *Life Will Get Better* so you can keep the concepts and strategies handy

- List of the preferred vendors and resources we use and recommend at my clinic

- Implementation guide to help you prioritize the strategies and approaches you want to use with your child

- And more …